COLLECTIONS
FOR YOUNG SCHOLARS™
VOLUME 6 BOOK I

Music and Musicians

Ancient Civilizations

Taking a Stand

Art by Gail Piazza

COLLECTIONS FOR YOUNG SCHOLARS™

VOLUME 6 BOOK I

PROGRAM AUTHORS
Carl Bereiter
Ann Brown
Marlene Scardamalia
Valerie Anderson
Joe Campione

CONSULTING AUTHORS
Michael Pressley
Iva Carruthers
Bill Pinkney

OPEN COURT PUBLISHING COMPANY

CHAIRMAN
M. Blouke Carus

PRESIDENT
André W. Carus

EDUCATION DIRECTOR
Carl Bereiter

CONCEPT
Barbara Conteh

EXECUTIVE EDITOR
Shirley Graudin

MANAGING EDITOR
Sheelagh McGurn

PROJECT EDITOR
Nita Garvin

ART DIRECTOR
John Grandits

VICE-PRESIDENT, PRODUCTION
AND MANUFACTURING
Chris Vancalbergh

PERMISSIONS COORDINATOR
Diane Sikora

COVER ARTIST
Gail Piazza

Printed in the United States
of America

ISBN 0-8126-6148-6

10 9 8 7 6 5

ACKNOWLEDGMEN[TS]

Grateful acknowledgment is given to the following publishers and copyright owners for permission granted to reprint selections from their publications. All possible care has been taken to trace ownership and secure permission for each selection included.

David Berreby: "The Man Who Wrote *Messiah*" by David Berreby, from the April 1992 issue of *Reader's Digest*, copyright © 1992 by David Berreby.

Broadside Press: "Martin Luther King Jr." by Gwendolyn Brooks from *Black Out Loud: An Anthology of Modern Poems by Black Americans*, edited by Arnold Adoff, copyright © 1970 Arnold Adoff, copyright © 1970 The Macmillan Co.

Carolrhoda Books, Inc., Minneapolis, MN: "Lady Merida" from *Stories from the Blue Road* by Emily Crofford, text copyright © 1982 by Emily Crofford. An excerpt from *A Pianist's Debut: Preparing for the Concert Stage* by Barbara Beirne, copyright © 1990 by Carolrhoda Books, Inc.

Joan Daves Agency, as agent for the heirs to the Estate of Martin Luther King, Jr.: An excerpt from "I Have a Dream" by Martin Luther King, Jr., from *A Testament of Hope: The Essential Writings of Martin Luther King, Jr.*, edited by James Melvin Washington, copyright © 1963 by Martin Luther King, Jr., copyright renewed © 1991 by Coretta Scott King.

Dial Books for Young Readers, a division of Penguin Books USA Inc.: "The Pretty Pennies Picket" from *Philip Hall Likes Me, I Reckon Maybe* by Bette Greene, text copyright © 1974 by Bette Greene.

Dillon Press, an imprint of Macmillan Publishing Co.: An excerpt entitled "Sweeping Pittsburgh Clean" from *Making Headlines: A Biography of Nellie Bly* by Kathy Lynn Emerson, copyright © 1989 by Dillon Press.

Doubleday, a division of Bantam Doubleday Dell Publishing Group, Inc.: "What Is Music?" from *Music Is My Mistress* by Edward Kennedy "Duke" Ellington, copyright © 1973 by Duke Ellington, Inc.

HarperCollins Publishers: *The Nightingale* by Hans Christian Andersen, translated by Eva Le Gallienne, illustrated by Nancy Ekholm Burkert, translation copyright © 1965 by Eva Le Gallienne, illustrations copyright © 1965 by Nancy Ekho[lm] from *His Majesty, Queen Hatshepsut* [by Dorothy] Carter, text copyright © 1987 by Dor[othy]

Houghton Mifflin Co.: "The Great Music[...] Myths by Olivia Coolidge, copyright 1949, [...] © renewed 1977 by Olivia E. Coolidge.

Alfred A. Knopf, Inc.: "On Hearing a Flute at Ni[ght] the Wall of Shou-Hsiang" by Li Yi from *The Jade Mountain*, translated by Witter Bynner, copyright 19[...] copyright © renewed 1957 by Alfred A. Knopf, Inc. "T[he] Weary Blues" from *Selected Poems of Langston Hughes* by Langston Hughes, copyright 1926 by Alfred A. Knopf, Inc., copyright renewed 1954 by Langston Hughes.

Lodestar Books, an affiliate of Dutton Children's Books, a division of Penguin USA Inc.: An excerpt entitled "Broken Bird" from *Come Sing, Jimmy Jo* by Katherine Paterson, copyright © 1985 by Katherine Paterson.

Margaret K. McElderry Books, an imprint of Macmillan Publishing Co.: "The Search for Early Americans" from *Searches in the American Desert* by Sheila Cowing, copyright © 1989 by Sheila Cowing.

Melissa Milich: "Mr. Einstein's Violin" by Melissa Milich from the January 1994 issue of *Cricket* magazine, copyright © 1994 by Melissa Milich.

Pantheon Books, a division of Random House, Inc.: "The Sound of Flutes" by Henry Crow Dog from *The Sound of Flutes and Other Indian Legends*, edited by Richard Erdoes, illustrated by Paul Goble, copyright © 1976 by Richard Erdoes and Paul Goble.

The Aaron M. Priest Literary Agency, Inc.: An excerpt entitled "Ray and Mr. Pit" from *Brother Ray: Ray Charles' Own Story* by Ray Charles and David Ritz, copyright © 1978 by Ray Charles and David Ritz.

Marian Reiner: "Music" and "What Is Jazz?" from *What Is That Sound!* by Mary L. O'Neill, text copyright © 1966 by Mary O'Neill.

continued on page 381

🎵 6 🎵

ANCIENT CIVILIZATIONS

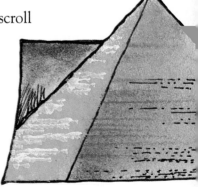

TAKING A STAND

MUSIC AND MUSICIANS

THE
NIGHTINGALE

Hans Christian Andersen
translated by Eva Le Gallienne
illustrated by Nancy Ekholm Burkert

In China, you know, the Emperor is Chinese, and all his subjects are Chinese too. This all happened many years ago, but for that very reason the story should be told. It would be a pity if it were forgotten.

The Emperor had the most beautiful palace in all the world. It was built of the finest porcelain and had cost a fortune, but it was so delicate and fragile you had to be very careful how you moved about in it.

The garden was full of exquisite flowers; on the rarest and most beautiful, tiny silver bells were hung, so that people passing by would be sure to notice them. Indeed, everything in the Emperor's garden had been most ingeniously planned, and it was so large that the gardener himself didn't know the full extent of it. If you kept on walking long enough, you came to a wonderful forest with great trees and fathomless lakes. The forest grew all the way down to the deep blue sea; the trees stretched their branches over the water, and large ships could sail right under them. Here lived a nightingale who sang so sweetly that even the poor fisherman—who had so much else to attend to—would stop and listen to her as he drew in his nets at night. "How beautiful that is!" he would say; then he had to get back to his work and forget about the bird. But the next night when he came to tend his nets and heard her singing, he would say again, "How beautiful that is!"

Travelers from all over the world came to the Emperor's city. They were filled with admiration for it, and for the palace and the garden. But when they heard the Nightingale, they all exclaimed, "That's the loveliest thing of all!"

When they returned home the travelers told all about their visits, and the scholars wrote many books describing the city, the palace, and the garden—but not one of them forgot the Nightingale; they kept their highest praise for her. And those who could write poetry wrote exquisite poems about the Nightingale who lived in the forest by the deep blue sea.

These books went all over the world, and at last some of them reached the Emperor. He sat in his gold chair reading and reading, every now and then nodding his head with pleasure when he came to an especially magnificent description of his city, his palace, and his garden. "But the Nightingale is the loveliest thing of all!" the books said.

"What's this?" cried the Emperor. "The Nightingale? I've never heard of her! To think that there is such a bird in my Empire—in my very own garden—and no one has told me about her! I have to read about her in a book! It's positively disgraceful!"

So he sent for his Chamberlain, who was so very haughty that if anyone of inferior rank dared to address him or ask him a question, he only deigned to answer, "Peh!"—which of course means nothing at all!

"I understand there is a highly remarkable bird here called the Nightingale," said the Emperor. "They say she is the loveliest thing in my whole Empire! Why has no one told me about her?"

"I've never heard that name before," answered the Chamberlain. "She's not been presented at Court, I'm sure of that."

"I want her to come here this very evening and sing for me!" said the Emperor. "It seems the whole world knows that I possess this marvel, yet I myself know nothing about her!"

"No! I have never heard that name!" the Chamberlain repeated. "But I shall look for her, and most certainly shall find her!"

But where was he to look?

He ran up and down all the staircases, through all the halls and corridors, asking everyone he met about the Nightingale—but no one knew anything about her. At last he ran back to the Emperor and told him it must be some fantastic

story invented by the people who write books. "Your Imperial Majesty shouldn't pay attention to everything that's written down. It's mostly pure imagination."

"But I read this in a book sent me by the High and Mighty Emperor of Japan—therefore it must be true! I insist on hearing the Nightingale. She must be here this very evening! I am graciously inclined toward her—and if you fail to produce her you'll all get your stomachs punched immediately after supper!"

"Tsing-peh!" cried the Chamberlain, and he started running again, up and down the staircases, through all the halls and corridors, and half the Court went with him, for they didn't want to have their stomachs punched—particularly after supper!

They inquired right and left about the marvelous Nightingale, who was known all over the world but had never been heard of by the courtiers in the palace.

At last they found a poor little girl working in the kitchen. She said, "Oh, the Nightingale! I know her well! How beautifully she sings! Every evening I'm allowed to take some scraps of food to my poor sick mother who lives down by the shore. On my way back I feel tired and sit down to rest a moment in the forest, and then I hear the Nightingale! She sounds so beautiful that tears come to my eyes; it's as though Mother were kissing me!"

"Little kitchen maid," said the Chamberlain, "I'll see that you're given a permanent position in the palace kitchen, and you shall even be allowed to watch the Emperor eat his dinner, if only you will lead us to the Nightingale, for we have been ordered to bring her here this evening!"

So, accompanied by half the Court, they set out toward the forest where the Nightingale was usually heard singing. After they had walked some way they heard a cow mooing. "Ah! There she is!" cried the courtiers. "What a powerful voice for such a little creature! But we seem to have heard her before!"

"That's only a cow mooing," said the little kitchen maid. "We still have a good way to go."

Some frogs began croaking in the marshes.

"Lovely!" exclaimed the Court chaplain. "I hear her! She sounds just like little church bells!"

"Those are the frogs croaking," said the kitchen maid. "But we ought to hear her soon."

And then the Nightingale began to sing.

"There she is!" said the little girl. "Listen! Listen! She's up there. Do you see her?" And she pointed to a little gray bird perched high up in the branches.

"Is it possible?" said the Chamberlain. "I never thought she'd look like that! She's so drab and ordinary. . . . But perhaps the sight of so many distinguished people has caused her to lose color!"

"Little Nightingale!" the little kitchen maid called out. "Our gracious Emperor would like to hear you sing!"

"With pleasure!" said the Nightingale, and sang so that it was a joy to hear her.

"It's like the tinkling of crystal bells," said the Chamberlain. "And look at her little throat—how it throbs! It seems odd that we've never heard her before. She'll have a great success at Court!"

"Shall I sing for the Emperor again?" asked the Nightingale, who thought the Emperor must be present.

"Most excellent little Nightingale!" said the Chamberlain. "It is my pleasure to invite you to appear at Court this evening, where you will delight His Imperial Majesty with your enchanting song!"

"It sounds best out in the forest," replied the Nightingale, but she consented to go willingly since it was the Emperor's wish.

The palace had been scrubbed and polished until the walls and the floors, which were made of porcelain, sparkled in the light of thousands of golden lamps. The finest flowers, those with the silver bells on them, were placed in all the corridors. There was such a coming and going, and such a draft, that all the little bells tinkled so loudly you couldn't hear yourself speak.

In the middle of the Great Presence Chamber, where the Emperor sat on his throne, a golden perch had been placed for the Nightingale. The entire Court was assembled, and the little kitchen maid, who had received the title of Assistant-Cook-to-His-Imperial-Majesty, was allowed to stand behind the door.

The courtiers were dressed in their grandest clothes and they all stared at the little gray bird, to whom the Emperor nodded graciously.

And the Nightingale sang so exquisitely that tears came to the Emperor's eyes and trickled down his cheeks. Then the Nightingale sang even more beautifully—it was enough to melt your heart. The Emperor was so delighted he wanted to give the Nightingale his gold slipper to wear around her neck. But the Nightingale declined the honor with many thanks; she felt she had been sufficiently rewarded.

"I have seen tears in the Emperor's eyes. What could be more precious to me? An Emperor's tears have a mysterious power! I have been amply rewarded!" And she sang again in that sweet, ravishing voice of hers.

"What delightful coquetry!" exclaimed the Court ladies, and they filled their mouths with water and made gurgling sounds in their throats whenever anyone spoke to them. They imagined they were nightingales too! Even the lackeys and the chambermaids admitted to being quite pleased—and that's saying a lot, for they are the most difficult people in the world to satisfy. Yes! The Nightingale was a great success!

From then on she had to remain at Court. She had a cage of her own, and was granted permission to go out twice during the day and once at night; but she had to be accompanied by twelve servants, who each held on tightly to a silk thread fastened to her leg. There wasn't much fun in that kind of an outing!

The whole city talked of nothing but the wonderful bird, and when two people met, one of them had only to say

"Nightin" for the other to say "gale"; then they would sigh in perfect understanding. Eleven shopkeepers' children were named after the Nightingale—but not one of them could sing a note, and they were tone-deaf into the bargain.

One day a large parcel arrived for the Emperor, and on it was written, "Nightingale."

"I expect it's a new book about our famous bird!" said the Emperor; but it wasn't a book at all. It was a wonderful example of the jeweler's art, lying in a velvet-lined case—an artificial nightingale that was supposed to be a copy of the real one, only it was encrusted with diamonds, rubies, and sapphires. When you wound it up, it sang one of the real Nightingale's songs and its tail moved up and down and glittered with silver and gold; around its neck was a little ribbon with the inscription, "The Emperor of Japan's nightingale is poor compared with that of the Emperor of China."

"How marvelous!" they all cried; and the messenger who had brought the artificial bird was immediately given the title of Chief-Imperial-Nightingale-Bringer.

"Now let us hear them sing together—what a duet that will be!"

So they sang together, but it didn't turn out very well, for the Nightingale sang in her own free way, while the artificial

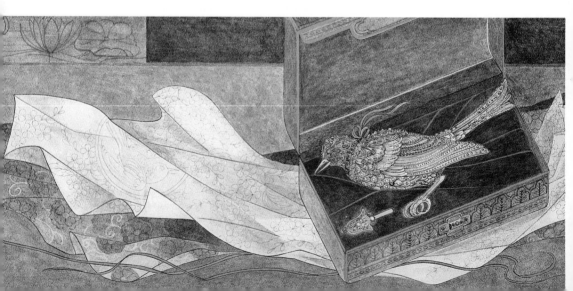

bird's song was stilted and mechanical. "The new bird is in no way to blame," said the music master. "It keeps perfect time and obeys all the rules of my special method." Then the artificial bird sang by itself and had just as great a success as the real one. And it was so much more beautiful to look at! It sparkled and shimmered like some fantastic jewel.

It sang its one and only tune thirty-three times without ever getting tired. The courtiers would have liked to hear it over and over again, but the Emperor felt it was the real Nightingale's turn to sing a bit. But where was she? No one had noticed, in all the excitement, that she had flown out of the open window, back to her own green forest.

"Here's a nice state of affairs!" cried the Emperor. The courtiers were all furious and accused the Nightingale of rank ingratitude.

"Well! After all, we still have the better of the two birds!" they said. So the artificial nightingale was made to sing again, and though they now heard the tune for the thirty-fourth time, they still hadn't quite caught on to it—for it was very difficult. The music master was loud in his praise of the artificial bird and said it was much better than the real Nightingale, for its outer covering of diamonds concealed the most delicate and intricate of mechanisms.

"You see, ladies and gentlemen—and first and foremost, Your Imperial Majesty!—the real Nightingale is totally unpredictable; she sings on the spur of the moment, and there's no way of knowing what you're going to hear. Whereas with the artificial bird everything has been regulated beforehand. You get just what you expect; there are no surprises! The mechanism can be logically explained. You can take the bird apart and examine the intricate wheels and cylinders, how one minute cog fits into another, causing it to sing. It's amazing what human skill and ingenuity are able to accomplish!"

"You're absolutely right!" they all agreed, and the very next Sunday the music master was authorized to demonstrate the bird to the common people. "They must hear it sing too," said the Emperor. So they did hear it and were so delighted they seemed quite intoxicated, as though they'd drunk too much tea—for that's what the Chinese drink, you know. They all exclaimed, "Oh!" held up their forefingers, and nodded their

heads. But the poor fisherman who had heard the real Nightingale sing said, "Yes! It's pretty enough; it's a fairly good imitation, but there's something lacking—I can't explain just what it is!"

The real Nightingale was banished from the Empire.

The artificial bird was kept on a silk cushion by the Emperor's bed. Around it were placed all the presents that had been sent to it, all made of gold and precious stones. Its title had been raised to High-Imperial-Bedside-Table-Singer, First-Class-on-the-Left. The Emperor considered the side nearer his heart to be the more distinguished—for an Emperor's heart is on the left, like everybody else's.

The music master wrote five-and-twenty tomes about the artificial bird, so long-winded and so learned and so full of the most complicated phrases that though everybody read them no one could understand a word; but of course they didn't dare admit it—they didn't want to appear stupid, for that would have meant having their stomachs punched, and they didn't like the thought of that!

In this way a whole year passed. By now the Emperor, the Court, and all the Chinese people knew every note and every trill of the artificial bird's song, and they enjoyed it all the more for that; now they were able to join in the singing, which of course they did. Even the street urchins sang, "Zeezee, zee! Gloo, gloo, gloo!" and the Emperor sang it too. It was all perfectly delightful!

But one evening, when the artificial bird was singing away and the Emperor lay on his bed listening to it, something went "crack!" inside the bird—a spring had broken. There was a great whirring of wheels, and the song stopped.

The Emperor leaped out of bed and sent for his personal physician, but there was nothing he could do! So a watchmaker was summoned, and after a great deal of talk and a long and careful examination, he managed to fix the mechanism fairly well, but he said it shouldn't be used too often, as many of the cogs had worn down and would be almost impossible to replace. He couldn't guarantee that the song would ever be the same again. It was a tragic state of affairs! Only once a year was the artificial bird allowed to sing—and even that put quite a strain on it. But the music master made a little speech, full of complicated words, declaring that the song was just as good as ever; and of course that settled it. Everyone agreed it was just as good as ever!

Five more years went by, and the whole country was heavy with grief—for the people were devoted to their Emperor, and now he was sick and the doctors said he hadn't long to live.

A new Emperor had already been chosen, and the people stood outside in the street and asked the Chamberlain if there was any hope of their old Emperor getting well again.

"Peh!" said the Chamberlain, and shook his head.

The Emperor lay in his huge, magnificent bed, so cold and so pale that the courtiers thought him already dead, and they all dashed off to pay court to the new Emperor. The lackeys ran outside to gossip about it, and the chambermaids gave a large tea party. Thick felt had been laid down on the floors of all the halls and corridors to muffle the sound of footsteps; the palace was as quiet as a tomb. But the Emperor wasn't dead yet. He lay there stiff and pale in his magnificent bed with the long velvet hangings and the heavy gold tassels. High up

in the wall was an open window through which the moon shone down on him and on the artificial bird by his side.

The poor Emperor could hardly breathe; he felt something heavy weighing on his chest; he opened his eyes and saw that it was Death. He was wearing the Emperor's gold crown, and held the gold sword of state in one hand and the Imperial banner in the other; and from the folds of the heavy velvet hangings strange faces peered out—some hideous and evil, and others mild and gentle. They were the Emperor's good and bad deeds watching him as he lay there with Death weighing on his heart.

"Do you remember this?" they whispered to him one after another. "Do you remember that?" And they reminded him of many, many things—and the sweat stood out on his brow.

"I never knew about all that!" cried the Emperor. "Music! Music!" he shouted. "Strike up the great Chinese gong and drown out their voices!"

But the voices continued, and Death nodded his head, like a real Chinese, in agreement with all that was said.

"Music! Music!" the Emperor cried again. "Precious little golden bird, sing to me! Sing! I implore you, sing! I've showered you with gold and precious jewels. I even hung my gold slipper around your neck with my own hands. Sing to me now! Sing!"

But the bird was silent. It couldn't sing unless it was wound up, but there was no one there to do it. Death kept on staring at the Emperor with his great hollow eyes, and the silence grew more and more terrifying.

Suddenly, through the window, came the sound of an exquisite song. It was the little, living Nightingale perched on a branch outside. She had heard of the Emperor's suffering and had come to bring him hope and comfort with her song. As she sang the phantoms gradually faded away, the blood began to flow more swiftly through the Emperor's feeble body, and Death himself listened and said, "Keep on singing, little Nightingale! Keep on!"

"Yes! If you will give me the golden sword! If you will give me the Imperial banner! If you will give me the Emperor's golden crown!"

And Death gave up the treasures one by one for each song the Nightingale sang. She sang of the peaceful churchyard where the white roses bloom, where the air is sweet with the scent of the elder tree, and where the green grass is moistened by the tears of those who have lost their loved ones. And, as he listened, Death was filled with a great longing to be back in his own garden, and he vanished out of the window like a cold white mist.

"Thank you, thank you!" said the Emperor. "You heavenly little bird—I know you now! I chased you out of my country, out of my Empire. And with your song you have chased the hateful dreams from around my bed; you have driven Death from my heart. How can I ever repay you, lovely bird?"

"You have repaid me," said the Nightingale. "The very first time I sang to you, you gave me your tears—I shall never forget that! Those are the jewels that gladden a singer's heart. But go to sleep now, and wake up well and strong! I'll sing to you!"

The Nightingale sang, and the Emperor fell into a deep sleep; a gentle, refreshing sleep.

When he awoke the next morning the sun was shining through the window, and he felt well and strong again; none of his servants had come back to him, for they thought he was dead, but the Nightingale was still singing.

"You must never leave me!" cried the Emperor. "You need only sing when you feel like singing, and I shall smash the artificial bird into a thousand pieces."

"Don't do that!" said the Nightingale. "It did the best it could! Keep it with you. I can't settle down and live here in the palace, but let me come and go as I like. I'll sit on the branch outside your window and sing to you, so that your thoughts may be serene and joyful; I'll sing of happy people and of those who suffer; I'll sing of the good and evil all around you which is kept hidden from you; for the little songbird flies far and wide—to the poor fisherman, and the peasant in his hut, to all those who are far away from you and from your Court. I love your heart much better than your crown, yet I venerate your crown, for there is an aura of sanctity about it! I shall come and sing for you—but one thing you must promise me!"

"Anything!" said the Emperor, who stood there in his Imperial robes, which he had put on all by himself, holding the heavy golden sword against his heart.

"I ask only one thing of you: Let no one know you have a little bird who tells you everything. It will be much better so!"

And the Nightingale flew away.

The servants and the courtiers came in to attend their dead Emperor. They were struck dumb with amazement when they saw him standing there; and the Emperor said to them, "Good morning!"

MEET HANS CHRISTIAN ANDERSEN, AUTHOR

Hans Christian Andersen changed the style and substance of traditional fairy tales by creating imaginative stories that combined folklore with personal experience. Throughout his career, the Danish-born author wrote nearly two hundred fairy tales. Some were based on his life. The Ugly Duckling is thought to reflect Andersen's experiences as a poor and unpopular youth who eventually became a distinguished author and the pride of his countrymen. In some tales, Andersen expressed his ideas about life. In The Nightingale, Andersen expressed his distaste for the cold precision of science as opposed to the beauty and spontaneity of nature.

MEET NANCY EKHOLM BURKERT, ILLUSTRATOR

Nancy Ekholm Burkert thinks that illustrating a book is much like staging a play—designing the sets, the costumes, and the lighting and "casting" the characters. Before she ever puts pen or brush to paper, she visualizes the characters and the location of the story. "If my drawings illuminate and expand the story as the author intended, I am fulfilled. If my drawings please the children for whom the stories were written, I am joyful!"

Burkert's full-color illustrations for The Nightingale were done with brush and India inks.

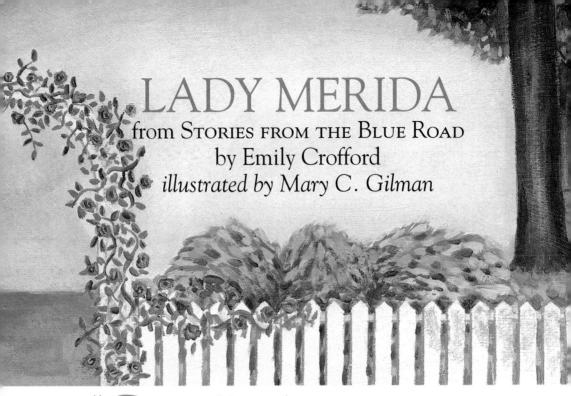

LADY MERIDA

from STORIES FROM THE BLUE ROAD
by Emily Crofford
illustrated by Mary C. Gilman

"Cross over," Josie said.

Her commanding tone aggravated me and I didn't see any reason to walk on the far side of the road just because Mrs. Merida was playing the piano. But which side of the road we walked on didn't seem like a big enough reason to fight with my best friend. I crossed over.

Mrs. Merida lived with Mr. Limon, the plantation owner, and her daughter, the lady from England he had married. Josie remembered the first Mrs. Limon, who had died before my family moved to Arkansas. "It depressed him so bad," Josie had told me, "that he went across the ocean for a vacation—and came back with a new wife."

People didn't say anything in front of Mr. Limon—times were too hard to chance getting put off the plantation—but his mother-in-law made a fine subject for talk behind his

back. Some said Mrs. Merida was moonstruck, others came right out with crazy. And she had cancer. They said the cancer and the craziness went together.

Mrs. Merida never visited neighbors or went to the store or to the post office, but some of the kids had seen her walking in the Limons' flower garden. And everybody had heard her playing the piano, which they cited as proof of her madness. Not that we hadn't heard pianos—including the one at school, there were four on the plantation—but none of them sounded anything like Mrs. Merida's. Her music whispered and thundered, stroked and lashed, danced and wept. It made me dream, made me restless, made my heart and my mind yearn for something beyond their ken.

"She's really . . ." Josie traced a little circle by her temple when we were past the house.

Set in a grove of oak trees, the Limon house was painted white and had a screened front porch. There were shrubs too, and roses climbing a trellis, and a curving sandy walkway to the front steps. I looked back over my shoulder at the house, walking as slowly as I could so I could hear the piano.

"Mother says she's just eccentric," I said. Mother had never met Mrs. Merida, but she knew Mrs. Limon and liked her.

Josie bounced her hair, which was thick and wavy and the color of a red squirrel. "Well, Papa says she's crazy—and I guess he knows."

Josie's father, Mr. Tomkin, was a ginner, an important position on the plantation. She said that was why he knew all about the lives of the other important people. I liked Mr. Tomkin, but I didn't think it was very nice of him to talk about Mrs. Merida.

Josie put her face so close to mine I could count her freckles. "And furthermore, he says that terrible disease she has is contagious." She bounced her hair again. "That's why she never visits anybody, or even goes to the post office."

Josie's know-it-all attitude and her bossiness really bothered me. Lately it had gotten worse, as if she was trying to see how far she could push me. But I didn't like to argue and I didn't know what to say in Mrs. Merida's defense—for all I knew, maybe Mrs. Merida's disease *was* contagious—so I kept quiet.

After I got home I waited until Bill and Correy went outside to play. Then I told Mother what Mr. Tomkin had said about Mrs. Merida's illness being contagious. Mother was setting up the ironing board and she jerked the legs so hard I thought they would break.

"That's bosh and nonsense!" she exploded. "Cancer is not contagious!" Pulling one of my school dresses over the ironing board, she said, "Meg, would you sweep the kitchen. The clothes have been sprinkled so long they're going to mildew if I don't get them done."

"Sure," I said. I knew she would return to the subject. She only wanted to make the right sentences in her head.

Mother took a flatiron off the stove and touched it with a tongue-moistened finger. The moisture sizzled, she began to iron, and the kitchen filled with a clean, starchy smell.

"People don't mean to be cruel," she said. "It's just that Mrs. Merida and her music are different, so they don't understand them. What they don't understand, they fear; and what they fear, they disparage."

I didn't know the word disparage, but if I asked what it meant she would just tell me to look it up. I had a fair idea about the meaning from the way she had used it, though, so I nodded and reached the broom under the table to sweep out some cornbread crumbs.

"Actually," I told her, "I think Mrs. Merida's music is wonderful, even if you can't clap your hands or sing to it. I don't care what Josie says."

Mother worked the iron around the dress collar. "So do I. Sometimes late at night, when it's still, I can hear it through the bedroom window—so beautiful, so filled with passion." She gave a sad little sigh. "I think Mrs. Merida must play when she's in pain."

"I'd give anything if I could play the piano like that," I said.

"Then why don't you ask her to give you lessons?"

I stopped sweeping and stared at Mother. Even though I didn't believe most of them, considering the number of stories, Mrs. Merida must be at least a wee bit mad. Besides, she was a very important person, and she lived in a very important house. Just thinking about going there was scary . . . and kind of exciting.

Mother set the cooled flatiron back on the stove and picked up the other one. "Meg, believe me—there's nothing to be alarmed about. In fact, the one way Josie's own mother defies her husband is to visit Mrs. Merida."

This time I figured Mother had gotten some wrong information. I couldn't imagine Josie's spiritless, dried-up little mother defying Mr. Tomkin. She could be in the middle of fixing supper and Mr. Tomkin would call from his easy chair in the living room, "Sarah, bring me a glass of water," and without a word she'd stop her work and take him the water. I thought of Mrs. Tomkin as a servant when I thought of her at all.

"Mrs. Tomkin and Mrs. Merida are friends," Mother was saying. "But you must not mention that to anybody—especially not to Josie. Mr. Tomkin pretends he doesn't know, and as long as he thinks no one else knows, it's all right."

I was going to ask her to repeat slowly what she had just said, but the boys charged through the back door, Correy chasing Bill, and ran right through my nice pile of dirt. I threw the broom after them, but I wasn't really all that angry. I knew now how to stand up to Josie! And I would learn to play the piano at the same time.

The next afternoon I left Josie standing on the other side of the road and went up the sandy walkway through the grove of oak trees to the Limon house. Josie had tried to talk me out of it and said she might walk with Peggy's group from now on if I went. That scared me, but it also made me more determined.

It was reassuring to find that the Limons' screened porch creaked just like the porch on our Blue Road house. Mrs. Limon answered my knock. Up close I could see why Mr. Limon had brought her from England. She looked like a movie star, with creamy skin and cornflower-blue eyes.

Clutching my books so tightly that my arm cramped, I stammered, "I—I'm Meg Weston. I wanted to—to talk to your mother about, uh, taking piano lessons."

"Why, yes," she said. "If Mama—that is, nothing like this has happened before."

"Dorothy," a voice behind her said, "will you get out of the doorway so the girl can come in." I liked their accents and wished I could talk that way.

"Hello, Mrs. Merida," I said.

"Lady Merida. Lady Rose Merida."

"Yes, Ma'am, Lady Merida."

She was wearing a soft and shimmery gray dress that went all the way to the floor, but it was only old fashioned, not crazy. She had not torn out hunks of her own hair, as I had heard, and there was no blood dripping from her fingertips either. Her nails were just painted with bright red polish.

Feeling more confident, I continued my inspection. I wanted to be able to describe Lady Merida to Mother. She was terribly thin. Her gray, tightly curled hair topped a small face, and her pale skin was drawn tight over her bones.

Then Lady Merida stepped toward me and my confidence dissolved. Her fierce gaze made the hairs on the back of my neck stand straight out.

"Well, I—I didn't think you would, I mean could, Ma'am. I mean, Lady Merida. I know you're busy." I backed toward the door, ready to run the instant I reached it.

She thrust out a bony hand as if to grab me. "Wait!"

I stopped in my tracks, too terrified to move, and stared at the hand. Blue veins stood out beneath thin white skin, the sinews from her knuckles to her wrists looked like cords, and her red fingernails were filed almost to the quick.

"You want to learn to play. You shall learn!" She pointed her index finger at the piano bench, and on legs more wooden than theirs I moved to it. She sat down beside me. "Put down your books," she said, and added scornfully, "The piano is played with *both* hands."

My hands were shaking so badly, I was sure she'd say something about them, but she didn't, and I quickly forgot my terror during the next thirty minutes as she taught me the connection between the notes on the music sheet, the keys, and my fingers. I was learning fast, I thought. Soon I would be playing like Lady Merida. Once I laughed aloud with the joy of my accomplishment and she smiled a little.

"Did you know I was a concert pianist?" she asked suddenly. She scooted me off the end of the bench and ran her fingers up and down the keyboard. Her hands no longer looked ugly but incredibly graceful. I visualized my own hands moving swiftly over the keys, imagined people around me gasping with admiration.

It started then, the kind of music that made people walk on the other side of the road. "What am I playing?" she demanded.

Drops of sweat crept down from my hairline. Somewhere buried inside all the extra notes I recognized the tune to a song I had heard the older kids singing, but I couldn't remember the title.

"Well, what? They must teach you something at that school."

"It's something about she doesn't love him anymore," I said. "Love has . . ."

Her hands stopped in mid-air; her mouth opened with such horror that it pulled the skin even more tightly over her face.

"That," she said in a quiet, dreadful tone, "is Beethoven's great and immortal Concerto No. 5. The *Emperor* Concerto." She folded her fingers into her palms, then flung them outward. "Blackguards who write asinine tripe to masterpieces should be hanged!" She began to play with the force of her whole body. The piano seemed to be alive, to be breathing its own fury. "Bloody thieves!"

The notes swelled, vibrated, wrapped themselves around me, filled my ears, burst into the space behind my eyes.

Mrs. Limon came in quickly from another room, took my arm, and guided me toward the door. Lady Merida, although she didn't turn to look at me or slow her racing fingers, ordered, "Come back tomorrow. Same time."

The next day I learned to stretch my fingers beyond their reach. When I protested that they wouldn't spread any further, Lady Merida took my hands and showed me that they

would. Then she placed my fingers on the keyboard. "Practice!" she said. "Stretch them. Practice!"

Since I didn't have anywhere else to practice playing except at Lady Merida's, she made me spend part of each lesson running up and down scales and playing the same pieces over and over. I didn't mind at first, but after two weeks of the same exercises, it seemed to me that Lady Merida should let me stop doing them. She wouldn't. In fact, when I complained that the exercises were boring she made me practice an extra ten minutes.

But I kept going for the lessons, almost every day except for the times Mrs. Limon met me at the door and told me her mother didn't feel well.

Josie tried everything to get me to quit. I told her playing the piano was important to me and that she might as well give up.

Actually, I was tired of going so often for the lessons. I missed out on a lot of after-school talk. I especially missed standing around in the post office with Josie and the other kids, including boys, while we waited for Miss Hettie, the postmistress, to come back with the mail after meeting the afternoon train.

I had been going for the lessons for a month when I realized that I hadn't really wanted to learn to play the piano. I had wanted to make the piano sound like Lady Merida made it sound. If Josie would stop bullyragging me about going for the lessons, I could quit. I didn't think Lady Merida would mind too much. Sometimes she got a pained expression on her face when I played.

Josie didn't give up, though. She got angry every time I told her good-bye at the Limon house. And finally she said, "I'm going to get myself a new best friend."

I shrugged as if I didn't care, but the truth was that it made me feel sick all over. Josie liked to get her way, she had a quick temper, and she could be mean. But she was more fun than anybody I knew, and she always stuck up for me. There were times when I felt closer to her than to my own family. We could freely tell each other our hurts and dreams, be silly or serious, say we despised somebody without feeling guilty. But even as I told myself that all I had to do was say I wouldn't go anymore, I turned into the Limons' without a word.

Josie kept walking. I stopped before I reached the oak grove to watch her back and the way the sun seemed to set her hair aflame, and she turned around.

"I was," she said—and I heard a quiver in her voice—"going to ask you to stay all night."

"Sure," I said. "If it's all right with Mother. I'd rather spend the night with you than anything." I took a deep breath. "I'm still going for the lesson, though."

"Okay," Josie said. "Come as soon as you can."

I thought about running to hug Josie and talk with her about what we would do that night. School had let out an hour early for a teacher's meeting, and Lady Merida wouldn't be expecting me yet. But Josie had almost caught up with some other kids, so I went on up the walk.

If I hadn't told Lady Merida I would be there, I would have gone home. I had won! I had made Josie understand that my letting her be the leader didn't mean she could bullyrag me. Besides, the air had become light with spring, the sun gifted everything with lazy warmth, and taking a piano lesson inside was the last thing I wanted to do.

Before I reached the porch, I heard the piano and knew immediately that someone other than Lady Merida was playing it. This music was timid and sweet. Starting across the creaky porch, I peered through the partially opened front door. The woman sitting at the piano saw me, jumped up, and darted through the kitchen and out the back way. Mrs.

Tomkin, I thought dizzily. Josie's mother! She did visit Lady Merida. She not only visited, she played the piano! She could make music! I realized that Lady Merida was watching me and closed my mouth.

"Since you're here," she said acidly, "come in."

The minute I walked into the living room, she pounced. "You're just like the rest! Insensitive! She"—she pointed a withered arm in the direction Mrs. Tomkin would be taking home through the field— "has the soul of an artist. If she hadn't been deprived as a child, if she wasn't married to that, that . . ."

"He is not either," I said, which surprised me because I never talked back to grown-ups. "Mr. Tomkin is funny—and nice." It was true. Mr. Tomkin had never ignored me like some adults did. He asked me kindly about school and my grades and my favorite subjects.

Her eyes still locked with mine, Lady Merida seemed to be asking herself a question. "Yes," she said. "Yes, I'm going to show you something."

She left the room and returned with a small, framed watercolor. It was so lovely—mountains and sky and sunlit grasses and wildflowers swaying in a breeze—that I sucked in my breath. Since, as Mother told me, I could never win at cards because my face showed everything, Lady Merida knew that I thought the watercolor was beautiful.

"Sarah Tomkin painted this from a childhood memory of her Ozark Mountains," Lady Merida told me. "Up until now I have been the only one on this plantation who knows she has this talent—because she's been ridiculed so often."

We were silent for a minute, and when she spoke again her voice sounded squeezed out. "She can't even read. I don't try to teach her, but she's drawn to the piano like a hungry child."

Instead of giving me my lesson, Lady Merida served us tea in china cups and not-very-sweet cookies that she called biscuits. She talked on and on, sometimes growing bitter about "thieves" who stole not only music but the soul as well. She talked of her childhood, told me about concerts she had played and men who had loved her, and described how the English countryside looked in the spring.

"Meghann," Lady Merida said, and I didn't tell her Meg came from Margaret, "there's nothing wrong with playing church songs and the old familiars, but *listen* to great music, with your senses and with your heart, all the days of your life."

I knew what she was saying, that I would never become a good pianist, and I didn't think it was fair. I had done everything she had told me. Besides, it was one thing for me to think about quitting. It was quite another for Lady Merida to suggest it, and I was certain she was about to.

"You mean you want to stop teaching me?"

She looked into her teacup, which was almost empty, and with a strange little smile said, "No, ducky, I don't want to stop teaching you." She went with me to the door, something she had never done before. "But perhaps not so often, eh? Say— once a week?"

I ran most of the way home, until I got a stitch in my side, and asked Mother if I could spend the night at Josie's. When she said yes, I quickly did my chores, tossed my toothbrush and nightgown and a change of underwear into a pillowcase, and left for Josie's.

The minute I walked into her big, two-story house that had an indoor bathroom, I sensed the excitement and smelled chicken frying. I loved the commotion there, the seven children talking two and three at a time, the laughing and singing, even the arguing.

Mr. Tomkin sat in his easy chair making jokes and asking questions about school. Mrs. Tomkin, as always, moved like a phantom, constantly busy, seldom speaking. I had never really noticed her before, but now I realized that the faded hair she wore in a bun at the nape of her neck had probably once been as lush and red as Josie's. I kept looking for a chance to speak to her in private before supper, but the only time I came close, just as I was about to follow her into the pantry where she stored quarts of fruits and vegetables, Danny and James Lee, Josie's big brothers, came into the kitchen and started teasing me. Danny knelt down in front of me, took both my hands, and said, "Ah, Meggie, hurry and grow up so I can marry you."

Then James Lee spun me around and said, "Pay no attention to him, darling, he's fickle. You're *my* girl." My face turned red and I hit them and wished they would keep doing it.

For supper we had fried chicken heaped high on platters at each end of the table, mashed potatoes with milk gravy, two quarts of Mrs. Tomkin's butter beans seasoned with bacon drippings and chopped onion, and watermelon rind preserves. We all said how good it was, Mr. Tomkin first.

"I would like a bit of variety, though," he said, then beamed around the table as if he had a wonderful idea. "I tell you what, let's all save our pennies and buy Mother a cookbook for Christmas."

He had always made remarks like that, and I had credited him with a fine wit, never before seeing below the surface. Knowing as I did now that Mrs. Tomkin couldn't read, I thought that Lady Merida should have gone ahead and called him whatever bad word she'd had in mind. The kids laughed, as they always did when he said something he expected them to laugh at, but this time I understood that some of them—especially Danny and James Lee—laughed out of nervousness.

They were afraid to displease Mr. Tomkin. Across from me Danny's biceps jerked after he put his hands in his lap where they wouldn't show. I knew his hands were making fists and that he would like to hit his father.

After supper I got my chance to speak alone with Mrs. Tomkin. Mr. Tomkin and the boys had gone out to slop the pigs. I had drawn scraping the dishes so I'd finished first. The girls were washing and drying and putting away. I heard Mrs. Tomkin going upstairs and quietly followed her. She had her hand on the doorknob to her and Mr. Tomkin's room when I reached the upstairs hall.

"Mrs. Tomkin," I said in a low voice, "Lady Merida showed me the watercolor you did."

She looked around like a frightened deer to see if anybody had heard.

"It's very beautiful," I said.

She blushed and a delicate smile fluttered over her lips.

"Thankee," she said.

When I went to Lady Merida's the next week, I had made up my mind to tell her I couldn't come anymore until fall. After-school softball season had started and I was trying out for sixth-grade pitcher. Josie was trying out for pitcher too, and I really wanted to beat her out. She was not as bossy anymore, but she still had a know-it-all attitude. She said she knew how to slow pitch and fast pitch and how to fake out a batter—that I didn't stand a chance.

Mrs. Limon came to the door. "Mama won't be able to give you lessons anymore, Meg," she said in a shaken voice. "She's very ill."

As I walked toward home, the gravel crunching under my shoes seemed to be saying, "She's dying, she's dying." I looked out over the flat land to where the tree line seemed to cut jagged pieces out of the sky and wondered why I was so upset. Lady Merida had never been patient with me like my teachers at school. She hadn't smiled with pride the way my parents did when I tried hard. We hadn't been friends like Josie and I were. She was not kin I was bound to love whether I liked her or not.

Still trying to figure it out, I turned onto the Blue Road and the crunching changed to a softer, sadder, earthy sound. I went down the grassy bank to the drainage ditch. Violets were growing beside the water. I picked a bouquet and wrapped their stems in a maple leaf I caught as it floated past.

All the way back to Lady Merida's I kept making up speeches, but when Mrs. Limon opened the door, all I said was, "These are for Lady Merida."

"How did you know?" she said. "Violets are her . . . her favorite."

She was going to cry. I glanced away and caught my own reflection in a window glass. My face was streaked with dust and tears.

Nothing had ever stirred the plantation up like what happened when Lady Merida died. She left her piano to Mrs. Tomkin. Not only that, but when Mr. Tomkin tried to sell it, Mrs. Tomkin told him that if he did he'd never get another meal in that house. Now people began to walk on the other side of the road when they passed the Tomkins'. I could sort of see why they did. Take the day Mrs. Tomkin told Josie and me to get our hoes and help weed the garden. She started hoeing and singing like she had a fever. She had changed her hair too. Instead of the bun at the back of her neck, now she plaited it into a crown.

Glowering at me, Josie said, "*You* might have come out all right, but she caught it—at least the crazy part. She's been like this ever since that lady passed on."

Mrs. Tomkin must have heard her, because she leaned her hoe against the garden fence and said, "Come into the house, the both of ye. I'm goin' to play my pieanna. My pie-anna," she said again, wonderingly, "what Lady Merida give me."

She marched into the house. Josie and I trailed behind her, past Mr. Tomkin, who sat forward in his easy chair and asked nervously, "What's the matter, Sarah? It come on you again? You think you better lay down and let the girls fix supper?"

"Hush up," she said.

She sat down at the piano and began to play, at first gentle and timid, like rabbits hopping, then so natural and sweet that it brought a vision of mountain flowers swaying in the wind.

"What's she playing?" Josie whispered.

Josie might have beaten me out for pitcher on the softball team, but she didn't know a thing about music.

"A concerto," I whispered back, and stood there listening with my senses and my heart while the music rose and soared out the window and climbed toward heaven.

MEET EMILY CROFFORD, AUTHOR

Emily Crofford grew up in a rural community where there was "much poverty and bigotry and physical illness." She describes her growing-up years as a personal struggle to overcome these problems. Out of her struggle came self-discipline, self-worth, and a strong belief that how one lives and what one does makes a difference.

The importance of such values often becomes the subject of Crofford's stories. In "Lady Merida," learning to play the piano has a profound effect on Mrs. Tomkin's self-image and this, in turn, changes her behavior significantly.

Crofford says, "In all my writing, I try to give hope. . . . The humor, beauty, dignity, and caring I have encountered during my life beg to be shared."

MEET MARY C. GILMAN, ILLUSTRATOR

Mary C. Gilman uses people she knows as models for her illustrations. She photographs them doing some of the things the characters do in the story she's illustrating. Gilman used two models for Lady Merida. One is a young piano teacher; the other, an elderly woman who also plays the piano. Gilman herself is the model for Lady Merida's daughter. Illustrations of Josie and Meg were based on two girls who live in Gilman's neighborhood.

When Gilman develops her illustrations, she refers to the photographs she has taken, but her characters are not direct copies of the photographs. Gilman paints her illustrations with acrylic paints.

Just like the characters in "Lady Merida," Gilman considers music an important part of her life. She likes to listen to classical music as she works in her studio.

THE GREAT MUSICIAN

from GREEK MYTHS
by Olivia Coolidge
illustrated by Rebecca Guay

I n the myth of Orpheus, the Greek love of music found
its fullest expression. Orpheus, it is said, could make such
heavenly songs that when he sat down to sing, the trees
would crowd around to shade him. The ivy and vine
stretched out their tendrils. Great oaks would bend their
spreading branches over his head. The very rocks would
edge down the mountainsides. Wild beasts crouched harm-
less by him, and nymphs and woodland gods would listen to
him enchanted.

Orpheus himself, however, had eyes for no one but the
nymph, Eurydice. His love for her was his inspiration, and
his power sprang from the passionate longing that he knew
in his own heart. All nature rejoiced with
him on his bridal day, but on that very
morning, as Eurydice went down to
the riverside with her maidens to
gather flowers for a bridal garland,
she was bitten in the foot by a

snake, and she died in spite of
all attempts to save her.

Orpheus was inconsolable.
All day long he mourned his
bride, while birds, beasts, and
the earth itself sorrowed with
him. When at last the shadows
of the sun grew long, Orpheus
took his lyre and made his way to the yawning cave which
leads down into the underworld, where the soul of dead
Eurydice had gone.

Even grey Charon, the ferryman of the Styx, forgot to ask
his passenger for the price of crossing. The dog, Cerberus, the
three-headed monster who guards Hades' gate, stopped full in
his tracks and listened motionless until Orpheus had passed.
As he entered the land of Hades, the pale ghosts came after
him like great, uncounted flocks of silent birds. All the land
lay hushed as that marvelous voice resounded across the mud
and marshes of its dreadful rivers. In the daffodil fields of Elysium the happy dead sat silent among their flowers. In the farthest corners of the place of punishment, the hissing flames
stood still. Accursed Sisyphus, who toils eternally to push a
mighty rock uphill, sat down and knew not he was resting.
Tantalus, who strains forever after visions of cool water, forgot
his thirst and ceased to clutch at the empty air.

The pillared hall of Hades opened
before the hero's song. The ranks of
long-dead heroes who sit at Hades'
board looked up and turned their
eyes away from the pitiless form of

Hades and his pale, unhappy queen.
Grim and unmoving sat the dark
king of the dead on his ebony
throne, yet the tears shone on his
rigid cheeks in the light of his ghast-
ly torches. Even his hard heart,
which knew all misery and cared nothing for it, was touched by the love and
longing of the music.

At last the minstrel came to an end, and a long sigh like
wind in pine trees was heard from the assembled ghosts.
Then the king spoke, and his deep voice echoed through
his silent land. "Go back to the light of day," he said. "Go
quickly while my monsters are stilled by your song. Climb
up the steep road to daylight, and never once turn back.
The spirit of Eurydice shall follow, but if you look around at
her, she will return to me."

Orpheus turned and strode from the hall of Hades, and
the flocks of following ghosts made way for him to pass. In
vain he searched their ranks for a sight of his lost Eurydice.
In vain he listened for the faintest sound behind. The barge
of Charon sank to the very gunwales beneath his weight,
but no following passenger pressed it lower down. The way
from the land of Hades to the upper world is long and hard,
far easier to descend than climb. It was dark
and misty, full of strange shapes and
noises, yet in many places merely black
and silent as the tomb. Here Orpheus
would stop and listen, but nothing
moved behind him. For all he could

hear, he was utterly alone. Then he
would wonder if the pitiless Hades
were deceiving him. Suppose he
came up to the light again and
Eurydice was not there! Once he
had charmed the ferryman and the
dreadful monsters, but now they had
heard his song. The second time his spell
would be less powerful; he could never go again.
Perhaps he had lost Eurydice by his readiness to believe.

Every step he took, some instinct told him that he was
going farther from his bride. He toiled up the path in reluc-
tance and despair, stopping, listening, sighing, taking a few
slow steps, until the dark thinned out into greyness. Up
ahead a speck of light showed clearly the entrance to the
cavern.

At that final moment Orpheus could bear no more. To go
out into the light of day without his love seemed to him
impossible. Before he had quite ascended, there was still a
moment in which he could go back. Quick in the greyness
he turned and saw a dim shade at his heels, as indistinct as
the grey mist behind her. But still he could see the look of
sadness on her face as he sprung forward saying, "Eurydice!"
and threw his arms about her. The shade dissolved in the
circle of his arms like smoke. A little whisper
seemed to say, "Farewell," as she scattered
into mist and was gone.

The unfortunate lover hastened
back again down the steep, dark
path. But all was in vain. This time

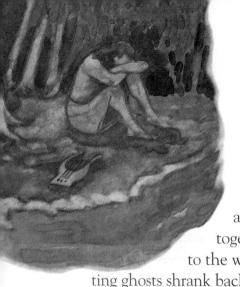

the ghostly ferryman was deaf to his prayers. The very wildness of his mood made it impossible for him to attain the beauty of his former music. At last, his despair was so great that he could not even sing at all. For seven days he sat huddled together on the grey mud banks, listening to the wailing of the terrible river. The flitting ghosts shrank back in a wide circle from the living man, but he paid them no attention. Only he sat with his eyes on Charon, his ears ringing with the dreadful noise of Styx.

Orpheus arose at last and stumbled back along the steep road he knew so well by now. When he came up to earth again, his song was pitiful but more beautiful than ever. Even the nightingale who mourned all night long would hush her voice to listen as Orpheus sat in some hidden place singing of his lost Eurydice. Men and women he could bear no longer, and when they came to hear him, he drove them away. At last the women of Thrace, infuriated by Orpheus' contempt, fell upon him and killed him. It is said that as the body was swept down the river Hebrus, the dead lips still moved faintly and the rocks echoed for the last time, "Eurydice." But the poet's eager spirit was already far down the familiar path.

In the daffodil meadows he met the shade of Eurydice, and there they walk together, or where the path is narrow, the shade of Orpheus goes ahead and looks back at his love.

ORPHEUS WITH HIS LUTE

William Shakespeare
illustrated by Rebecca Guay

Orpheus with his lute made trees,
And the mountain tops that freeze,
Bow themselves when he did sing.
To his music plants and flowers
Ever sprung, as sun and showers
There had made a lasting spring.

Every thing that heard him play,
Even the billows of the sea,
Hung their heads and then lay by.
In sweet music is such art,
Killing care and grief of heart
Fall asleep, or hearing, die.

(*King Henry VIII*, Act III, scene i)

THE SOUND OF FLUTES

retold by Henry Crow Dog
illustrated by Paul Goble

Well, you know our flutes, you have heard their sound and seen how beautifully they are made. That flute of ours, the *Siyotanka*, is a very peculiar instrument. It is made for only one kind of music—love music. In the old days, the young men would sit by themselves, maybe lean against a tree in the dark of the night, hidden, unseen. They would make up their own special tunes, their courting songs.

We Indians have always been shy people. A young man hardly could screw up his courage to talk to a *wincincala*—the pretty girl he was in love with—even if he was a brave warrior who had already counted coup upon an enemy.

There was no privacy in the village, which was only a circle of tipis. No privacy in the family tipi either, which was always crowded with people. And, naturally, you couldn't just walk out into the prairie, hand in hand with your girl, to say sweet words to each other. First, because you didn't hold hands—that would be very unmannerly. You didn't show your affection—not by holding hands anyway. Second, you didn't dare take a walk with your wincincala because it wasn't safe. Out there in the tall grass you could be gored by a buffalo, or tomahawked by a Pawnee, or you might run into the U.S. Cavalry.

The only chance you had to meet the one you loved was to wait for her at daybreak when the young girls went to the river or brook with their skin bags to fetch water. Doing that was their job. So, when the girl you had your eye on finally came down the water trail, you popped up from behind some bush, and stood so that she could see you—and that was about all you could do to show her that you were interested— stand there grinning foolishly, looking at your moccasins, scratching your ear, humming a tune.

The wincincala didn't do much either, except get very red in the face, giggle, fiddle with her waterbag, or maybe throw you a wild turnip. The only way she could let you know that she liked you, too, was for her to take a long, long while to do her job, looking back over her shoulder a few times, to peek at you.

So the flutes did all the talking. At night, lying on her buffalo robe in her father's tipi, the girl would hear the soulful, haunting sound of the Siyotanka. She would hear the tune made up

especially for her alone, and she would know that out there in the dark a young man was thinking about her.

Well, here I am supposed to relate a legend and instead I am telling you a love story. You see, in all tribes, the flute is used as an expression of a young man's love. It has always been so. And whether it is Sioux, or Pawnee, or Cheyenne, or Shoshone, the flute is always made of cedar wood and shaped like the long neck and the head of a bird with an open beak. The sound comes out of the beak. There is a reason for this, and that's where the legend comes in.

Once, untold generations ago, the people did not know how to make flutes. Drums, rattles, bull-roarers, yes—but no flutes. In these long-past days, before the white man came with his horse and firestick, a young hunter went out after game. Meat was scarce, and the people in his village were hungry. He found the tracks of an elk and followed them for a long time. The elk is wise and swift. It is the animal that possesses the love-charm. If a man has elk medicine, he will win the one he loves for his wife. He will also be a lucky hunter.

Our poor young man had no elk medicine. After many hours, he finally sighted his game. The young hunter had a fine new bow and a quiver made of otterskin full of good, straight arrows tipped with points of obsidian—sharp, black, and shiny like glass. The young man knew how to use his weapon—he was the best shot in the village—but the elk always managed to stay just out of range, leading the hunter on and on. The young man was so intent on following his prey that he hardly took notice of where he went.

At dusk the hunter found himself deep inside a dense forest of tall trees. The tracks had disappeared, and so had the elk. The young man had to face the fact that he was lost and that it was now too dark to find his way out of the forest. There was not even a moon to show him the way. Luckily, he found a stream with clear, cold water to quench his thirst. Still more luckily, his sister had given him a rawhide bag to take along, filled with *wasna*—pemmican—dried meat pounded together with berries and kidney fat. Sweet, strong wasna—a handful of it will keep a man going for a day or more. After the young man had drunk and eaten, he rolled himself into his fur robe, propped his back against a tree, and tried to get some rest. But he could not sleep. The forest was full of strange noises—the eerie cries of night animals, the hooting of owls, the groaning of trees in the wind. He had heard all these sounds before, but now it seemed as if he were hearing them for the first time. Suddenly there was an entirely new sound, the kind neither he nor any other man had ever experienced before.

It was very mournful, sad, and ghostlike. In a way it made him afraid, so he drew his robe tightly about him and reached for his bow, to make sure that it was properly strung. On the other hand, this new sound was like a song, beautiful beyond imagination, full of love, hope, and yearning. And then, before he knew it, and with the night more than half gone, he was suddenly asleep. He dreamed that a bird called *Wagnuka*, the redheaded woodpecker, appeared to him, singing the strangely beautiful new song, saying, "Follow me and I will teach you."

When the young hunter awoke, the sun was already high, and on a branch of the tree against which he was leaning was a redheaded woodpecker. The bird flew away to another tree and then to another, but never very far, looking all the time over its shoulder at the young man as if to say "Come on!" Then, once more the hunter heard that wonderful song, and his heart yearned to find the singer. The bird flew toward the sound, leading the young man, its flaming red top flitting through the leaves, making it easy to follow. At last the bird alighted on a cedar tree and began tapping and hammering on a dead branch, making a noise like the fast beating of a small drum. Suddenly there was a gust of wind, and again the hunter heard that beautiful sound right close by and above him.

Then he discovered that the song came from the dead branch which the woodpecker was belaboring with its beak. He found, moreover, that it was the wind which made the sound as it whistled through the holes the bird had drilled into the branch. "*Kola*, friend," said the hunter, "let me take this branch home. You can make yourself another one." He took the branch, a hollow piece of wood about the length of his forearm, and full of holes. The young man walked back to his village. He had no meat to bring to his tribe, but he was happy all the same.

Back in his tipi, he tried to make the dead branch sing for him. He blew on it, he waved it around—but no sound came. It made the young man sad. He wanted so much to hear that wonderful sound. He purified himself in the sweat-lodge and climbed to the top of a lonely hill. There, naked, resting with his back against a large rock, he fasted for four days and four nights, crying for a dream, a vision to teach him how to make the branch sing. In the middle of the fourth night, Wagnuka, the bird with the flaming red spot on his head, appeared to him, saying, "Watch me." The bird turned into a man, doing this and that, always saying, "Watch me!" And in his vision the young man watched—very carefully.

When he awoke he found a cedar tree. He broke off a branch, and working many hours hollowed it out delicately with a bowstring drill, just as he had seen Wagnuka do it in his vision. He whittled the branch into a shape of a bird with a long neck and an open beak. He painted the top of the bird's head red with *washasha*, the sacred vermilion color. He prayed. He smoked the branch with incense of burning sage and sweet grass. He fingered the holes as he had watched it done in his dream, all the while blowing softly into the end of his flute. Because this is what he had made—the first flute, the very first *Siyotanka*. And all at once there was the song, ghostlike and beautiful beyond words, and all the people were astounded and joyful.

In the village lived an *itancan,* a big and powerful chief. This itancan had a daughter who was beautiful, but also very haughty. Many young men had tried to win her love, but she had turned them all away. Thinking of her, the young man made up a special song, a song that would make this proud wincincala fall in love with him. Standing near a tall tree a little way from the village, he blew his flute.

All at once the wincincala heard it. She was sitting in her father's, the chief's, tipi, feasting on much good meat. She wanted to remain sitting there, but her feet wanted to go outside; and the feet won. Her head said, "Go slow, slow," but her feet said, "Faster, faster." In no time at all she stood next to the young man. Her mind ordered her lips to stay closed, but her heart commanded them to open. Her heart told her tongue to speak.

"*Koshkalaka, washtelake*," she said. "Young man, I like you." Then she said, "Let your parents send a gift to my father. No matter how small, it will be accepted. Let your father speak for you to my father. Do it soon, right now!"

And so the old folks agreed according to the wishes of their children, and the chief's daughter became the young hunter's wife. All the other young men had heard and seen how it came about. Soon they, too, began to whittle cedar branches into the shapes of birds' heads with long necks and open beaks, and the beautiful haunting sound of flutes traveled from tribe to tribe until it filled the whole prairie. And that is how Siyotanka the flute came to be—thanks to the cedar, the woodpecker, the wind, and one young hunter who shot no elk but who knew how to listen.

ON HEARING A FLUTE AT NIGHT FROM THE WALL OF SHOU-HSIANG

Li Yi
translated by Witter Bynner
illustrated by Jean and Mou-sien Tseng

The sand below the border-mountain lies like snow,
And the moon like frost beyond the city-wall,
And someone somewhere, playing a flute,
Has made the soldiers homesick all night long.

66

THE MAN WHO WROTE MESSIAH

David Berreby

illustrated by Joe Servello

Barren masts swayed in the wind alongside the mist-covered wharves of Chester, a port in western England. At the steamy, leaded window of the Exchange Coffee House, a large, heavyset man stood anxiously watching idle sailors stomping their feet in the cold. The wind was still unfavorable, and once again no packet boats would be setting out. Yet he had to get to Ireland, and soon.

Once, he had been the toast of Europe, its single most celebrated composer. But by this unpromising day in November 1741, George Frederick Handel was on the verge of financial, and perhaps even artistic, bankruptcy. He was barely one step ahead of his creditors, and his public had abandoned him.

He left the window, settled uneasily on a hard oak chair and puffed his pipe. It was a day made for glum reflection.

Music had been Handel's passport to the world ever since the day his father, a surgeon in the German town of Halle, had taken him as a youth to the court of Duke Johann Adolf at Weissenfels. His father wanted the boy to be a lawyer.

While the elder Handel attended to business at the court, George Frederick, bored, wandered into the palace chapel and began improvising on the organ. The sound of footsteps made him turn. Standing there, watching, was Duke Johann Adolf.

"Who," the Duke asked, "is this remarkable child?" Handel's father was summoned, and he was told that it would be a crime to make such a prodigy into a lawyer.

George Frederick was a quick study. While still in his teens he left Halle, first for Hamburg, then for Italy, where he mastered the art of composing operas. By his mid-20s, he had set his sights on London, with its lively musical life and money to spare for grand shows.

In 1711, *Rinaldo,* Handel's first opera in Italian for English audiences, played for a remarkable 15 nights to packed houses at the new Haymarket Theatre. It was a success such as the London musical scene had never known, and it launched Handel into society. Dukes and duchesses quit their country estates to hear the opera, and on the city's crowded streets those who had been lucky enough to get tickets whistled its tunes.

After Handel's "Te Deum" was performed at St. Paul's Cathedral to celebrate a peace treaty in 1713, Queen Anne granted Handel an annual stipend of 200 pounds. With that and his opera receipts, Handel was now probably the best paid composer in the world.

For good measure, Queen Anne's successor, King George I, added 200 pounds to the stipend. And the king also joined the company of many fashionable Londoners by investing thousands in Handel's opera company, the Royal Academy of Music.

The academy was the culmination of Handel's dream. Most musicians depended on handouts from aristocratic patrons. But Handel had learned to be both artist and

entrepreneur. Even as he composed, he recruited investors, engaged singers and performed various administrative duties. As long as his operas pleased the people, they would buy tickets, and the academy would turn a handsome profit.

Investing in Handel seemed a safe bet. At performances of *Amadigi* in 1715, the public kept clamoring to hear arias repeated until finally the theater management banned repetitions so the show could end before dawn. At the opening of *Radamisto* in 1720, unruly crowds fought to get at seats.

Those were the glory days, when all London buzzed with stories of how Handel had refused to be intimidated by patrons or celebrated singers. One tenor had threatened to jump headfirst into a harpsichord if Handel did not alter a tune. "That," the composer replied, "would be vastly more entertaining than your singing." And when a soprano announced she would not sing her part the way he'd instructed, Handel told her she would, or he would drop her out a window. Then he picked her up and headed for the nearest sill.

But by the mid-1720s, Handel's fortunes began fading. Audiences dwindled, and in 1728 the academy had to declare bankruptcy. Also that year, poet John Gay offered *The Beggar's Opera*, a parody of Italian opera, sung in English. It was a huge hit, and spawned a fad for shows with catchy music and English lyrics. The new craze was another nail in the coffin of Handel's Italian repertory.

But he kept on composing and doggedly producing his operas. In 1737 stress and overwork brought on an attack of the "palsy," which took away the use of four fingers of his right hand. Letters expressing concern about his decline flew across England and to the Continent. The future Frederick the Great of Prussia wrote his royal cousins in England, "Handel's great days are over, his inspiration is exhausted and his taste behind the fashion."

It was a desperate Handel who left England that summer for a cure at the famous hot springs of Aachen in Germany. There, he sat each day in the bubbling water. Little trays floated by bearing simple meals and snacks. It was a pleasant place, and it cheered him.

He had not been there long when one afternoon he left the baths and dressed quickly. Several hours later, he had not returned for his next treatment. The nuns who tended the spa grew concerned. Then, from the abbey church, came a burst of glorious music. Habits flying, the nuns ran to investigate. There was Handel, his health unaccountably restored, happily improvising on the organ.

But the return of Handel's health was not accompanied by a return of his operas to public favor. He was deep in debt, and his savings were exhausted by past operatic ventures.

For several years, he barely kept his head above water by giving concerts, as opera after opera failed. By the summer of 1741 Handel, age 56, must have wondered if the time had come to give up the stage altogether.

One morning a servant brought a thick bundle of papers, wrapped in parchment. It was a text assembled by one of Handel's wealthy admirers, a part-time poet named Charles Jennens.

Jennens had been trying for years to interest Handel in setting his words to music. He had already sent Handel a dramatization of the Biblical story of Saul and David. Handel wrote an oratorio, a sort of stripped-down opera performed by singers in ordinary clothes without scenery, but it was not a success. How could it be? No special effects, no grand costumes.

Handel surveyed this new script. Like Jennens's earlier effort, its plot was taken from the Bible. But this was different. The text actually *was* the Bible. Jennens had skillfully assembled Old and New Testament quotations into a stirring narrative of Christ's birth, sacrifice and resurrection. He had called the piece *Messiah*.

It began with a prophecy from Isaiah, promising deliverance: "Comfort ye, my people." Here were words of solace so simple and familiar that they seemed to draw melody from Handel as easily as he breathed. He was deeply inspired.

The Lord Lieutenant of Ireland had invited Handel to Dublin, to present a work for charity. Here was an occasion that would at least benefit those in greater need. Handel set to work.

He composed confidently. He began the *Messiah* on August 22, and 23 days later he was done. This music had given him something more precious than box-office appeal—it had given him hope.

Handel roused himself, paid his bill, and left the Chester coffee-house. He wandered back to the Golden Falcon Inn. It was a far cry from the palaces and spas to which he had been accustomed. As he entered his small room, he was again fighting despair. After so monumental an effort, was his music to be stopped by the exigencies of wind and tide? He went to bed with a troubled mind, trying to rekindle the hope that the miraculous composition had engendered in him.

The next morning the wind had changed!

Dublin's music-lovers were expecting something extraordinary. Handel had been rehearsing his new work for months, and now the leading newspaper was requesting that at the opening performance ladies not wear hoops in their skirts and "gentlemen come without their swords," to permit an extra 100 people to fit into the theater on Fishamble Street.

It was a hot, noisy crowd that Handel saw as he sat down at the harpsichord on April 13, 1742. He looked at his small force of instrumentalists and nodded. Without further ceremony, on the serene tones of its opening sinfonia, the *Messiah* entered the world.

Before it was over, the music had moved Dubliners to tears. Reviewers were ecstatic.

The next performance was so enthusiastically attended that panes of glass were removed to keep the hall from overheating. Best of all, the work proved a windfall for charity. Four hundred pounds went to hospitals and infirmaries, and 142 prisoners were freed from prison after the *Messiah* paid their debts.

But the London première of the *Messiah* on March 23, 1743, was a different story. Sermons were preached against it. Was the Bible a text to be sung by actors for mere entertainment? And the audience that *did* seek entertainment was disappointed by the lack of action and showy arias. Later, these opera zealots hired thugs to beat people who went to see Handel's works.

No matter, thought Handel. His renewed inspiration extended to other pieces. *Samson, Judas Maccabaeus* and the *Music for the Royal Fireworks* were all successes. He also had failures. But with renewed faith, he went about writing the

best music he could. When friends commiserated about the empty seats at a performance of *Theodora,* Handel shrugged and replied, "The music will sound the better."

Through thick and thin, Handel stubbornly clung to his beloved *Messiah,* offering it every year for charity during the last decade of his life. London audiences began to flock to the performances. When King George II heard the oratorio for the first time, the story goes, he could not contain his enthusiasm. As trumpets rang out in the great Hallelujah chorus, he rose to his feet. A stir went through the audience and, in a rustle of silks and clanking of swords, everyone else stood up. To this day, when the joyous strains of this chorus are heard, audiences in the English-speaking world stand.

The mysteriously powerful inspiration that gave birth to the *Messiah* restored Handel's wavering confidence and helped save him from ruin and obscurity. Though late in life he went blind, he still composed and played the organ. It was after the blind composer had conducted a performance of *Messiah* that he fainted and had to be carried home. He lingered through the night of Good Friday, April 13, 1759—17 years to the day after the *Messiah's* Dublin première. In the early-morning hours, George Frederick Handel died.

But to the delight of listeners of all faiths throughout the world, his *Messiah* lives.

BROKEN BIRD

from COME SING, JIMMY JO
by Katherine Paterson
illustrated by James Watling

Eleven-year-old James Johnson has been surrounded
by music all his life—the country music of his West Virginia
mountain home. He lives there with his grandmother while the
rest of the family—Grandpa, Uncle Earl, and James's parents,
Jerry Lee and Olive—are on the road with their singing group.
James plays the guitar and sings beautifully . . . for his
grandmother. He is afraid, at first, to perform before an
audience, but Grandma tells him, "You got the gift," and it is
James's responsibility to share it.

Now James has moved away from Grandma's
home to Tidewater, Virginia, where he and his family are
performing regularly on the Countrytime TV show. Things are
changing, becoming more difficult. No longer called James, he is
known as Jimmy Jo. His mother, Olive, is turning into an
ambitious performer named Keri Su. Needing a rest, James has
been anxiously awaiting the trip back to Grandma's for
Thanksgiving vacation.

🌿 *78* 🌿

J ames practically danced to the house Wednesday afternoon. It was as though since September he'd been seventy years old and suddenly, by some magic, had turned eleven again. No, five—back before he'd ever been to school, when all the world he really knew was that rocky hillside.

I'm just a poor—*toodletido*—wayfaring stranger—*tooka doodle doodley do*, he sang inside his head, jazzing it up with an imaginary fiddle obbligato and throwing in banjo, guitar, and mandolin as well. Travelin' through—*whang, whang, tooka doodle di doo*—this world of woe—This time the fiddle ornamentation was fancier than a Christmas tree. Oh, he wished it would all come out of his hands and mouth the way it sounded in his head—*toodledido toodledi tiddle di tiddle di*—

He danced right up the steps, into the house. "I'm here!" he yelled. "Let's go."

For a minute there was no answer, then Jerry Lee's voice from the kitchen. "Back here, boy. I'm not quite ready."

James bounced into the kitchen. Jerry Lee was standing at the counter slathering mayonnaise on bread. "Making us lunch so we won't have to stop so long."

"Good," James said. "Where's ever'body?"

Jerry Lee spread the mayonnaise very carefully to each corner of the bread. "We got this call from a club over to the Beach. Olive—Keri Su—thought it was too good a chance to pass up."

"I don't know what you mean."

Jerry Lee slapped the ham on the bread and slammed down the lid of the sandwich. "Yeah, well, it means that them three are going to stay here and play this club over the weekend."

"What about us?"

"Well, I don't know about you, old buddy, but if I don't get out of this burg and back to the mountains pretty soon, I may just wither away." He put the sandwich in a plastic bread wrapper with the others he had made and carefully folded up the loose end. After he had put the sandwiches and a couple of bananas and a bag of cookies in a paper sack, he turned back to James. "I told them I thought you'd rather go home with me."

"Sure," said James. He was sure, wasn't he? "Sure, of course." It was all he had thought about all week. "I'm ready anytime. Just let me get my stuff."

He sat close to Jerry Lee, not just because they'd have to go through the tunnel, but because he wanted to say with his body how glad he was to be going home with him. "How are they gettin' out to the Beach?" On the bridge it occurred to him that he and Jerry Lee were driving away in the only car.

"I rented 'em a Buick. Baby blue. It's her favorite color." He glanced over at James and smiled a crooked way that made James hurt for him. "Your momma was like a little girl with a new doll." He squinted at the road. "This old heap ain't got much going for it."

"It works fine."

Jerry Lee grinned and put his right arm around James and drew him even closer. "I reckon," he said. "Maybe so."

James wanted to say, *Don't be lonesome, I'm here with you.* But he couldn't. He tried to stay awake, though, in case Jerry Lee wanted to talk—he didn't . . . or sing—he didn't. They listened to the radio—all kinds of pop and rock, even caught the news and weather.

"The weatherman says it's going to be clear and sunny for the weekend," James said, in case Jerry Lee had missed it. "That's good, ain't it?"

"What?" Jerry Lee was on another planet.

"Clear and sunny. Ain't that good?"

"Yeah. Fine."

"I changed the dog's name" was first thing Grandma said after she'd hugged them and asked where everyone else was and pretended that it was just fine that only the two of them had come home for Thanksgiving.

"How come?" James asked, glad to change the subject.

"He can't sing on key, and it was giving him one of those inferior complexes to be the namesake of a famous country telly vee star when he couldn't sing a lick."

"Oh, Grandma."

"Yep. Order to keep him from sulking around with his tail between his legs, I had to change his name from James to what he does best—Squirt. He's a heap site happier now, ain't you, Squirt?"

Even Jerry Lee smiled. He hugged Grandma again. "How 'bout some hot biscuits and gravy for two starving hillbillies who ain't put their teeth into a real biscuit for nigh onto three months?"

"Oh, go off, you," she said, pleased as could be. She'd never say that Olive couldn't cook worth doodlydi-squat, but she didn't mind too much if someone else hinted at it.

James picked up the puppy and scratched his neck. He wanted to be loyal to Olive. He really did. She was his mother, and though she wasn't like other people's mothers, she loved him in her way, even when she was so set on being Keri Su and making him into Jimmy Jo. Like Jerry Lee said, she meant well. Besides, what did he know about other people's mothers anyway? The only mother he knew to speak of was Grandma, and she was a special case. Olive's mother had died when Olive was just a little girl. How was Olive supposed to know about mothers? Hadn't she made that chicken-feet soup when she thought he was sick? She told him it was what her mother had made her once. That's probably all she could remember about mothers—chicken-feet soup. And though no one said it right out clear, he was pretty sure that the reason she had run away from home was because her daddy beat her. A person like James, who had had Grandma and Jerry Lee loving him all his life, shouldn't be so hard on her, but still he forgot to be understanding when he looked at the hurting in Jerry Lee's face.

The next day while James and Grandma fixed the dinner, Jerry Lee chopped and split firewood until it reached the top of the shed and there was no place else to put it. Now and again Grandma would go to the window and peer out at him.

"I think he's upset 'cause the others didn't come home," James said. He felt a need to explain Jerry Lee to her.

"I 'speck that's it," she said, but she didn't sound convinced.

James was kneading the bread dough that he'd sneaked away from Grandma while she was staring out the window. He punched it down several times before he said, "I'm thinking I shouldn'ta gone down there with the Family."

"Oh?" She didn't look up from the onions she was chopping for the dressing.

"They fight about me a lot, Grandma."

"Who fights about you?"

"Well, Earl and Momma, mainly. Earl thinks I'm trying to shove him over, but I ain't, really I ain't."

"And your momma don't like Earl shoving back on you?"

"Not exactly." Now that she was asking him, he wasn't sure why Keri Su was so often mad. Her words said that it was Earl she was fighting with, but it wasn't as though she was trying to favor him over Earl. Actually, if he thought about it, she wasn't so thrilled when James took the lead, either. She liked it when he sang duets with her. In fact, the time he played sick, she'd seemed happier with him than when he was doing just what she said she wanted him to do. She went to a lot of trouble to make him that soup. She didn't usually go out of her way for him. "I can't figure Momma out," he said at last. "I don't know what she wants outta me."

"Maybe she don't know, either," Grandma said. Then, very softly, "She was always the star before, James. Now she's gotta share that with you." *Chop, chop, chop* on the cutting board and *crack* outside as Jerry Lee split still another log. "I know she loves you, but it ain't easy when you're still not more than a girl yourself to make room for another person, even when you love the other person."

James flipped and punched the springy dough. It was ready to put to rise, but he didn't want to let it go. It was warm under his hands, and the rhythm of slap, punch, turn, and dig with the heels of his hands was a comfort—but not comfort enough. Something was catching in his throat. "Well, what am I supposed to do?" he asked her. "I just make Momma and

Earl unhappy if I sing, but you and Daddy tell me I gotta do it because I got the gift. What am I supposed to do?"

She shook her head. "Nothin's ever pure, James. Joy and pain always show up in the same wrapper."

"Earl says she shoved you out."

Grandma looked up sharply. "I don't shove so easy," she said. "If I move over, it's 'cause I choose to."

"Didn't you want to sing no more?" The thought of never singing again was rising like a great spiked ball inside his gut.

Her face softened. "Nobody loved to sing more'n me," she said. "I woulda give anything to sing straight through to Glory without a pause. But my voice give out. You heard me. You know."

He didn't insult her by trying to say otherwise. He knew her voice was gone.

"That was just about the time that Olive come along. Poor waif. But she could tear up a song, even then. Afterward you was with me. It all worked out." She mixed the onions with the stale bread and melted butter and began stuffing the turkey Jerry Lee had brought her from Tidewater. James divided the dough, patted and folded half of it to rise in the loaf pan, and began making the other half into rolls.

Finally she said, "Is it just too miserable? Do you crave to stop?"

"No." He wouldn't look at her. "I don't crave to stop, but I wish you was with us."

"Well, that don't hurt my feelings none," she said, wiping her hands and putting the bird into the huge black oven. "Let's you and me give that feller out there a good weekend, awright?"

He put a dish towel over the rolls and set them on the back of the stove. "Whyn't I get the guitar and Autoharp, so's we can make us some music while ever'thing's cooking?"

"By cracky, Squirt, I think the boy is getting some sense at last."

They made a lot of music over the weekend. When they were too stuffed to breathe, they picked. Jerry Lee even tried the fiddle. Real fiddling is powerful hard, and Jerry Lee hardly dared play in front of them, much less in front of an audience, but he still practiced, hoping to be good enough someday. Grandma and James told him over and over how much he was improving, and that seemed to cheer him a bit.

They sang a lot of sad songs, too. It's funny about sad songs. They don't really make you feel sadder when you're down. They even seem to take the sting out of the worst of it.

"I've wrote me a new song," Jerry Lee said, pulling off the thumb and finger picks he used for rousing tunes. "Wanna hear it?" Of course they did. The music was gentle, with easy chords, so James and Grandma caught on to it and played backup after the first few lines. It was a song about an old man who lives alone in a tumbledown house in the hills. One day he finds a bird with a broken wing and takes it home and nurses it to health. Slowly, the bird gets well and begins to sing for the man, and the old cabin is filled with beauty. But when spring comes, the bird flies away. For the first time, the old man is lonely, because before the bird came and filled his house with song, he hadn't known that it was empty.

"That's about the prettiest song I ever heard in all my born days," said Grandma, wiping her eyes with her apron. "I swear, you gotta do that one on the telly vee."

"What do you think, James?"

"Oh, Daddy, it's beautiful," James said. And it was, so sad and pure that it rearranged his insides.

"I want you to sing it," Jerry Lee said.

"No." James said. "You should sing it. It's your song."

"I wrote it for you."

James looked from his father to his grandmother. "You think I can do it?" He didn't want "Broken Bird" to come across as some kiddy song. It would be awful for people to think of it as cute or darling.

"We'll teach you how to do it right, won't we, Jerry Lee?" And they did, stopping only to eat and sleep. They sang the song until it ran through his veins like rich, red blood. And he knew beyond a twinkle of doubt that "Broken Bird" belonged to him, and he could give it as a gift.

They hated to leave. All three of them cried a little, and the puppy whimpered to keep them company in their misery, still the road back was a happier one than the road there had been. He and Jerry Lee sang and joked, and James slept for long stretches of highway—no longer anxious for his daddy, just comfortable being near him.

They were late getting back Sunday night—later than they'd meant to be, as the holiday traffic on the bridge and in the tunnel was like a logjam on the South River. But the house was empty.

"Still at the club, I reckon," said Jerry Lee.

"Clubs is always late," agreed James, as if he knew.

He didn't see the others until he came home from school on Monday. Keri Su was in her pink quilted robe with the frilly collar, drinking coffee at the kitchen table.

He went straight back to where she sat. She was reaching out her arm, so he went close and let her kiss him on the cheek. She smelled heavily of perfume mixed with coffee.

"How's your trip, sugar?"

"Fine." He wasn't sure if he ought to say something about missing her, because in the end, he hadn't. But he had at first, so he said, a little stiffly, "I was sorry you and Earl and Grandpa couldn't go, too."

"I was sorry too, sugar, but we got this good gig over to the Beach."

He nodded. "Grandma says to tell you 'Hey.'"

"I guess she's spry as ever."

"Seemed to be fine," he said. What a stupid conversation. "Ever'body else gone?"

"Earl and Grandpa are sleeping. Jerry Lee's out somewheres."

He went to the refrigerator and stared into it. "Did Jerry Lee tell you he wrote me a new song for the show?"

"That's nice." She said it lightly, as though she didn't care. And she probably didn't just then.

It was after she had heard "Broken Bird" that Keri Su began to care.

"That ain't no little boy's song," she said.

"I wrote it for him," said Jerry Lee.

"Well, when he grows up, he can sing it," she said, turning to their manager, Eddie Switten, for help. "Don't you think that song needs more'n a kid's voice?"

Eddie was perched on the end of the sofa with his arms and legs crossed. "The boy done it great," he said. "I think it'll go over just fantastic."

"I'd like to try it," she said. "I'd just like y'all to hear me do it before you decide."

Eddie and Jerry Lee looked at each other. James could feel that Jerry Lee was angry, and he was sure of it when his daddy spoke very quietly. "How about Earl? Don't he want to try it, too?"

Earl shrugged. "Not my style." Then to James's surprise, he added, "C'mon, Keri Su, let the boy have the song."

She opened her mouth to say something, then shut it again.

"I want Wallace to hear the boy sing it," Eddie was saying. "If he says it don't suit, I ain't arguing."

But Wallace, the manager of the *Countrytime* TV show, liked it. When James got to the mike Friday night, he said, "This here's a new song that my daddy wrote for me, and I'm singing it for him." And he did, putting into the song all the

pain of the ride to West Virginia and the joy of their time there together. When he finished, he turned to Jerry Lee and held out his hand so they could take the bow together. His father's eyes were bright with tears.

It was funny how he didn't seem to mind the fans that night. In fact, it was as though he was standing in a glowing circle. He smiled at each one and signed their autograph books and scraps of paper. They weren't greedy and grabbing, but sad and lonely, their faces almost hungry. *Don't be sad. Don't be hungry.* He wanted to reach out to them all and heal their hurts. How rich he was. How full of good things. Jerry Lee had written a wonderful song, and James had opened his mouth, and the song had come to life. He had been possessed by it, as though it were a magic spell. The enchantment had

poured out from his body through the air—all the way to West Virginia. Maybe Grandma would call. He hoped she would, although he didn't need her to say that he had been good.

She did call, but all she did was cry, the puppy yowling with dismay in the background, until they both had to laugh. He went to bed without talking to anyone. He didn't want to talk anymore. He just wanted to lie there in the darkness, holding inside his body the fierce sorrow of the music. His fingers, his head, his chest, even his toes rang with it, and he could not hold it in. He had been swallowed by the hugeness, the greatness of it—like Jonah in the belly of the whale. The vastness filled him with wonder, but he was not afraid. This must be how it feels, he thought, this must be how it feels to have the gift.

MEET KATHERINE PATERSON, AUTHOR

Katherine Paterson writes about young characters who develop self-awareness and personal strength by overcoming stressful situations. Her books are set in the United States and China, where she spent her childhood, and in Japan, where she spent four years as a missionary.

Paterson once explained her success in writing for young people: "My gift seems to be that I am one of those fortunate people who can, if she works hard at it, uncover a story that children will enjoy."

The Music Lesson. 1943. Thomas Hart Benton.

Oil on canvas. Mrs. Fred Chase Koch Collection, Wichita, Kansas. © 1993 Thomas Hart Benton
and Rita P. Benton Testamentary Trusts/VAGA, NY

The poet Fujiwara no Yasumasa playing the flute by moonlight.
1882. Tsukioka Yoshitoshi.

Woodblock print. Private collection. Photo: Art Resource

FINE ART
MUSIC AND MUSICIANS

Saint Cecilia. c. 1880-1885. Sir Edward Burne-Jones design, executed by William Morris & Co.

Pot-metal glass and white glass with silver stain. Museum Purchase, Surdna Fund, The Art Museum, Princeton University

Blue and Green Music. 1919. Georgia O'Keeffe.

Oil on canvas, 58.4 cm. x 48.3 cm. Alfred Stieglitz Collection, Gift of Georgia O'Keeffe, The Art Institute of Chicago. 1969.835. © 1994 The Georgia O'Keeffe Foundation/ARS, NY. Photo: © 1992 The Art Institute of Chicago. All Rights Reserved

MUSIC
Mary L. O'Neill

Music is a tale told in sounds
Of such infinite reach
All time, all life, all tongues
Are in its speech.
Music is the sound of events
So moving, in its classic or its blue,
The heart nods recognition: "I was there.
And I have felt that, too . . ."

WHAT IS JAZZ?

Mary L. O'Neill

Jazz is a swoony
Syncopated beat
In through the eardrums
Out through the feet.
Rackety, coaxie,
Blast that beat
Whop it sassy
Sound it sweet
Clap, stomp, shout,
Blow surprise,
Shoot that trumpet
Till it cries
All the teardrops
In your eyes . . .

illustrated by
Lori McElrath-Eslick

THE SOLITARY REAPER

William Wordsworth
illustrated by Lori McElrath-Eslick

Behold her, single in the field,
   Yon solitary Highland Lass!
Reaping and singing by herself;
   Stop here, or gently pass!
Alone she cuts and binds the grain,
And sings a melancholy strain;
O listen! for the Vale profound
Is overflowing with the sound.

No Nightingale did ever chaunt
    More welcome notes to weary bands
Of travellers in some shady haunt,
    Among Arabian sands:
A voice so thrilling ne'er was heard
In spring-time from the Cuckoo-bird,
Breaking the silence of the seas
Among the farthest Hebrides.

Will no one tell me what she sings?—
    Perhaps the plaintive numbers flow
For old, unhappy, far-off things,
    And battles long ago:
Or is it some more humble lay,
Familiar matter of to-day?
Some natural sorrow, loss, or pain,
That has been, and may be again?

Whate'er the theme, the Maiden sang
    As if her song could have no ending;
I saw her singing at her work,
    And o'er the sickle bending;—
I listen'd, motionless and still;
And, as I mounted up the hill,
The music in my heart I bore,
Long after it was heard no more.

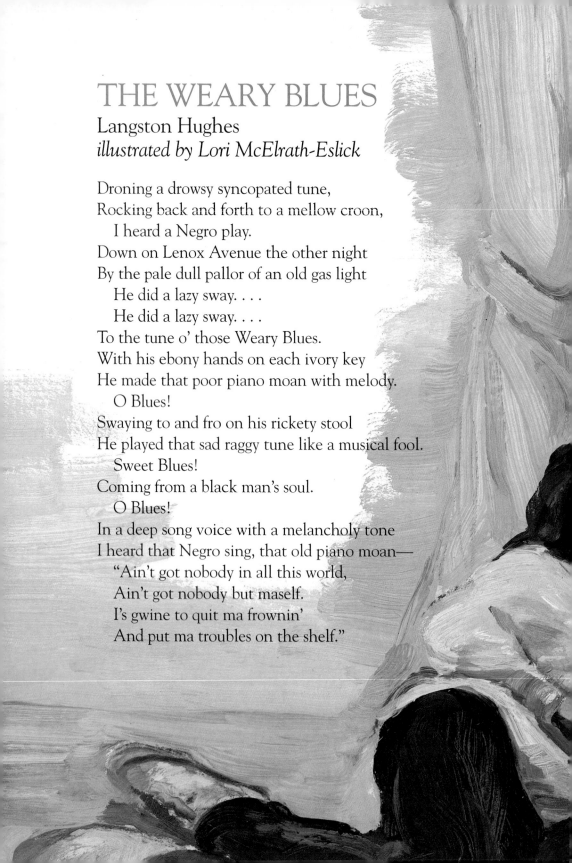

THE WEARY BLUES

Langston Hughes
illustrated by Lori McElrath-Eslick

Droning a drowsy syncopated tune,
Rocking back and forth to a mellow croon,
   I heard a Negro play.
Down on Lenox Avenue the other night
By the pale dull pallor of an old gas light
   He did a lazy sway. . . .
   He did a lazy sway. . . .
To the tune o' those Weary Blues.
With his ebony hands on each ivory key
He made that poor piano moan with melody.
   O Blues!
Swaying to and fro on his rickety stool
He played that sad raggy tune like a musical fool.
   Sweet Blues!
Coming from a black man's soul.
   O Blues!
In a deep song voice with a melancholy tone
I heard that Negro sing, that old piano moan—
   "Ain't got nobody in all this world,
   Ain't got nobody but maself.
   I's gwine to quit ma frownin'
   And put ma troubles on the shelf."

Thump, thump, thump, went his foot on the floor.
He played a few chords then he sang some more—
   "I got the Weary Blues
   And I can't be satisfied.
   Got the Weary Blues
   And can't be satisfied—
   I ain't happy no mo'
   And I wish that I had died."
And far into the night he crooned that tune.
The stars went out and so did the moon.
The singer stopped playing and went to bed
While the Weary Blues echoed through his head.
He slept like a rock or a man that's dead.

IN THEIR OWN WORDS

WHAT IS MUSIC?
from Music is My Mistress
by Edward Kennedy Ellington
illustrated by Gershom Griffith

Edward Kennedy Ellington was born in Washington, D. C., in 1899. Before he was even in high school, a friend decided that Edward should have an elegant-sounding title. He gave Edward the nickname by which he was known for the rest of his life: Duke. Until his death in 1974, Duke Ellington performed music with his band. The music was jazz, and he transformed it with a special Ellington sound that became world-famous. For fifty years, Duke Ellington was a major force in the music world. His influence is still felt.

What is music to you?
What would you be without music?

Music is everything.
Nature is music (cicadas in the tropical night).

The sea is music,
The wind is music,
Primitive elements are music, agreeable or discordant.

The rain drumming on the roof,
And the storm raging in the sky are music.

Every country in the world has its own music,
And the music becomes an ambassador;
The tango in Argentina and calypso in Antilles.

Music is the oldest entity.

A baby is born, and music puts him to sleep.
He can't read, he can't understand a picture,
But he will listen to music.

Music is marriage.

Music is death.

The scope of music is immense and infinite.
It is the "esperanto" of the world.

Music arouses courage and leads you to war.
The Romans used to have drums rolling before
    they attacked.
We have the bugle to sound reveille and pay homage
    to the brave warrior.

The Marseillaise has led many generations to victories
    or revolutions;
It is a chant of wild excitement, and delirium, and pride.

Music is eternal,
Music is divine.

You pray to your God with music.

Music can dictate moods,
It can ennerve or subdue,
Subjugate, exhaust, astound the heart.

Music is a cedar,
An evergreen tree of fragrant, durable wood.

Music is like honor and pride,
Free from defect, damage, or decay.

Without music I may feel blind, atrophied,
    incomplete, *inexistent*.

RAY AND MR. PIT
from BROTHER RAY: RAY CHARLES' OWN STORY
by Ray Charles and David Ritz
illustrated by Gershom Griffith

Ray Charles was born in Albany, Georgia, in 1930, and spent his boyhood in the little town of Greensville, Florida. When he was five, he began to lose his sight. He was blind by the age of seven. Ray Charles has never let his blindness interfere with his passion for music, and he began performing while still a teenager. His music is often called rhythm and blues, but he embraces many forms—from country-and-western to old-fashioned ballads—fashioning them with his unique style.

And then there was music. I heard it early, just as soon as I was seeing or talking or walking. It was always there—all shapes, all kinds, all rhythms. Music was the only thing I was really anxious to get out of bed for.

I was born with music inside me. That's the only explanation I know of, since none of my relatives could sing or play an instrument. Music was one of my parts. Like my ribs, my liver, my kidneys, my heart. Like my blood. It was a force already within me when I arrived on the scene. It was a necessity for me—like food or water. And from the moment I learned that there were piano keys to be mashed, I started mashing 'em, trying to make sounds out of feelings.

Sometimes I'm asked about my biggest musical influence as a kid. I always give one name: Mr. Wylie Pitman. I called him Mr. Pit.

Now you won't find Mr. Pit in any history of jazz . . . but you can take my word for it: Mr. Pit could play some sure-enough boogie-woogie piano. And best of all, he lived down the road from us.

Red Wing Café. I can see the big ol' red sign smack in front of me right now. That was Mr. Pit's place. It was a little general store where he and his wife, Miss Georgia, sold items like soda water, beer, candies, cakes, cigarettes, and kerosene. Mr. Pit also rented out rooms.

Mama and me were always welcome there and, in fact, during one period when we were really down and out, we lived at the Red Wing Café for a while.

Mr. Pit's place was the center of the black community in Greensville, and when you walked into the café you saw two things—right off—which shaped me for the rest of my life.

Talkin' 'bout a piano and a jukebox.

Oh, that piano! It was an old, beat-up upright and the most wonderful contraption I had ever laid eyes on. Boogie-woogie was hot then, and it was the first style I was exposed to. Mr. Pit played with the best of them. He just wasn't interested in a musical career; if he had been, I know he would have made it big. He just wanted to stay in Greensville and lead a simple life.

Well, one day when Mr. Pit started to playing, I waddled on up to the piano and just stared. It astonished and amazed me— his fingers flying, all those chords coming together, the sounds jumping at me and ringing in my ears.

You'd think an older cat would be put off by this young kid hangin' round. Not Mr. Pit. Maybe that's 'cause he and Miss

Georgia didn't have children of their own. But for whatever reasons, the man treated me like a son; he lifted me on the stool and put me right there on his lap. Then he let me run my fingers up and down the keyboard. That was a good feeling, and forty-five years later, it *still* feels good.

I tried to figure out how he could make all those notes come together. I was a baby, but I was trying to invent some boogie-woogie licks of my own.

Some days I'd be out in the yard back of the house. If I heard Mr. Pit knocking out some of that good boogie-woogie, I'd drop what I was doing and run over to his place. The man *always* let me play.

"That's it, sonny! That's it!" he'd scream, encouraging me like I was his student or his son.

He saw I was willing to give up my playing time for the piano, so I guess he figured I loved music as much as he did. And all this was happening when I was only three.

I couldn't spend enough time with that gentleman. I was there for hours—sitting on his lap, watching him play or trying to play myself. He was a patient and loving man who never tired of me.

"Come over here, boy, and see what you can do with this pie-ano," he'd say, always helpful, always anxious to teach me something new. And when I look back now, I know he saw something in me, felt something in me, which brought out the teacher in him.

The jukebox was the other wonder. There was a long bench at Mr. Pit's place, and I had my special place, right at the end, smack against the loudspeaker. That's where I would sit for hours, enthralled by the different sounds.

A PIANIST'S DEBUT
PREPARING FOR THE CONCERT STAGE
Barbara Beirne

My name is Leah Yoon, and more than anything else, I want to become a concert pianist.

I'm 11 years old, and I'm studying music at The Juilliard School in New York City. The music conservatory here is one of the best in the world. Pianist Van Cliburn, violinist Itzhak Perlman, and cellist Yo-Yo Ma all studied at Juilliard. I'm hoping that if I work hard enough, someday I'll have a career making music too.

I spend each Saturday from 9:00 A.M. to 6:00 P.M. at The Juilliard School. My program, the Pre-College Program, is for musicians who have not yet graduated from high school. Some of my classmates are only nine years old.

My first class is Chorus. Ms. Scott, the voice coach, tells us that singing and playing the piano are similar. When you sing, you have to control your breath so that you breathe only at the end of each singing phrase. If you breathe at other times in the music, it's like putting a period in the middle of a sentence. Your song will sound choppy, or it won't make sense.

Playing music on an instrument works the same way. Musical pieces are often divided into phrases, and if you breathe in the middle of a phrase, the sound and feeling of your music will change.

Solfège is my next course. Solfège is a French word, and it means using *do, re, mi, fa, sol, la,* and *ti* to sing musical notes. Our teacher, Ms. Thompson, has us sing musical pieces we don't know by sight-reading them. We read the notes on our sheet music and sing without stopping. It's hard to do, but it trains our eyes to move quickly. We learn to connect the

notes and rhythms on musical scores with the sounds they represent.

At other times, Ms. Thompson plays music on the piano, and we try to write down the notes she has played.

Chamber Music is another course we all have to take. Chamber music is music written to be performed by a small group in a person's home or in a small concert hall. In my chamber-music group, Rebecca plays the violin and Debbie plays the cello.

Playing in a music group is like playing on a baseball team. You have to depend on the other team members. If one musician doesn't play well, the music sounds terrible. So we learn to listen closely to each other and depend on each other's abilities.

Our teacher, Ms. Goldberg, says that this team effort will help all three of us "to expand our reach artistically." I think she means that we'll try harder because we don't want to disappoint our friends.

Another important course is Repertory Class. I take this from my Juilliard piano teacher, Ms. Carlson. In her class, everyone takes turns playing piano pieces. As one person plays, the others listen and watch carefully. Later we comment on the performances. Playing in front of an audience like this is good practice for our recitals at the end of the year.

To help me in my studies at Juilliard, I have a tutor named Mr. Kay. We often talk about music theory. He explains to me how chords and rhythms are put together and how other parts of music work. These things are difficult to understand, and sometimes it's almost like learning a foreign language.

At The Juilliard School, there is a feeling of intense competition between the students. We all know that only a few of us will ever make it to the concert stage.

Lately I've been watching some of the advanced students prepare for major competitions. My friend Eduardus Halim has applied for the Van Cliburn Competition in Fort Worth, Texas. He says that at least 250 pianists from 37 countries will apply to compete. Only 40 will be chosen. Everyone wants to be selected because the competition's winner will be invited to play on a long concert tour.

Someday, if my dream comes true, I'll be accepted for the Van Cliburn Competition.

During the week, I go to the Professional Children's School. This is a regular school where I study English and Math, and other subjects that are required. The thing that's different about my school is that all the students here are preparing for careers in the arts. Some are already working in their fields.

The hallways are filled with photographs of students who are actors, dancers, musicians, and models. Sometimes I see classmates on television. No one here treats me as if I'm different because I spend so much time at the piano.

Every day I practice the piano for at least five hours. I get up at 5:30 A.M. and practice for two hours before school. Then, in the afternoon, I practice from 3:00 P.M. to 6:00 P.M.

Before beginning I warm up my hands by playing scales. Then I try a piece I'm comfortable with. After I've worked for a while on things I know, I start on a new piece, always trying to build up my speed and dramatic intensity.

Practicing is not something I *have* to do—it's something I *want* to do. I love music. I'm happier when I'm playing the piano than at any other time. Some nights I can hardly believe it when it's time for dinner.

Pianists have to be very careful of their hands when they practice. Once, after a long stretch of hot and humid weather, the wires on my piano tightened, and the keys were hard to play. I strained my fingers. The doctor said that I had to stop playing the piano for two weeks. It was a long, lonesome 14 days. I felt as if I'd lost my best friend.

Thursday is the day I have a private lesson with my piano teacher Ms. Gray. Before we start, Ms. Gray and I usually talk about the piece of music I'm going to play. She says that it's important to understand the feelings the composer was trying to communicate, because I have to express these feelings to the audience through my performance.

Today I'm going to play "Kind Im Einschlummern," by Robert Schumann. The English translation is *Child Falling Asleep*. Robert Schumann loved to write musical compositions

about his children. In this piece, Schumann wanted his listeners to picture how beautiful a baby looks drifting off to sleep. When I play this piece, I think of my little cousin Mary in her crib. I play the notes softly, as if I'm trying not to wake her.

Ms. Gray is pleased with my interpretation, but she makes some suggestions about my playing.

"Remember your posture, Leah," she says. "Be a queen at the piano."

Ms. Gray has been a concert pianist herself. She stresses posture because when you sit with your back straight, you have the best possible reach and control of the keyboard. Good posture also helps you breathe properly.

Ms. Gray ends the lesson by assigning Beethoven's *Pathétique* Sonata. The music looks so difficult it makes me dizzy.

The weeks pass with the same schedule—practice, school, private lessons, and Saturdays at Juilliard. It won't be long now before my first New York recital. I can hardly wait.

One afternoon I attend a Master Class at Juilliard. At the class, Lev Vlasenko critiques the performances of five advanced

students. Mr. Vlasenko is a well-known pianist and teacher from the Soviet Union. As he talks to the students, the rest of us listen. He tells them:

Play with personality!
Take risks.
Put more of yourself into the music.
Do not be afraid.
Play with confidence.

I'm going to try to remember these suggestions for my recital.

Finally Ms. Gray gives me the good news. It's time to begin working on my recital piece. For the performance, Ms. Gray assigns me a work from Bach's *The Well-Tempered Clavier*. To learn more about my new assignment, I go to the New York Library & Museum of the Performing Arts, which is part of the public library at Lincoln Center. The library has a huge music department.

A copy of the original score of *The Well-Tempered Clavier* is in the research section. I check it to make sure the notes in my score are correct. I also take out some books that tell me about the piece. The word *clavier* means keyboard, and *well-tempered* refers to a system of piano tuning used in the early 18th century.

Then I find a surprise. Beethoven practiced *The Well-Tempered Clavier* when he was 12 years old. That really makes me feel good, since I'm only 11.

The library has many musical recordings, and I'm able to listen to famous pianists play my recital

piece. It's interesting to hear other musicians' interpretations. But I never, never try to imitate them. I want to develop a style of my own.

My favorite concert pianist is Alicia de Larrocha. She has a light and feathery style. When I was younger, I used to worry that my fingers would not grow long enough to reach certain chords. But then I discovered that de Larrocha has small hands. She said that having small hands made her learn to use her "musical imagination." Since many times she couldn't use other pianists' ways of fingering, she had to come up with her own ways of reaching for certain chords or notes. This makes her playing sound different from other pianists'.

I try hard to use my musical imagination. I experiment with various ways of playing until I'm perfectly happy with the sound I make. Sometimes I strike the keys harder or softer, or I use the pedals differently, or I try new fingerings.

During the weeks before my recital, I practice every free minute.

At last, the night of the performance arrives!

I wait in the wings until it's time to go onstage. There's a little hole in the stage door where you can peek out and watch the audience. My turn is coming up, so I take one last look at the score—but it's hard to concentrate. It seems like forever before the stage manager says, "You're on."

I walk out on the stage trying to look as calm and confident as possible. As I adjust the piano bench and sit down, I remember my teacher's words: "Be a queen."

Something happens when I start to play. A calm feeling comes, and I forget about the audience. It's almost as if I'm playing in my own living room.

I play my last note, and there's a silence.

Suddenly the applause starts. It goes on for a long time. I don't think I've ever felt happier than I do now. I want to shout, *HOORAY!* But instead I bow with as much dignity as I can.

I'm so lucky! I get to do what I love most— MAKE MUSIC.

I think the most important thing for young people going into classical music is that they must love it more than anything in the world. They must feel that without it their lives would be incomplete and that they have to have it at all costs and at all expense for the rest of their lives.

VAN CLIBURN

MR. EINSTEIN'S VIOLIN

Melissa Milich
illustrated by Cat Bowman Smith

In the fall of 1922 Mr. Albert Einstein came to Japan. I was just a little boy then, and people say, "How can you remember?" but I do.

Many guests came to our home during those years and sat in the great wingback chairs in my father's study. But only one bounced me on his knee. That was Mr. Albert Einstein.

There was much cause for celebration when Mr. Albert Einstein decided to visit Japan. Other scientists considered Mr. Einstein the greatest scientist in the world, even when they didn't understand the things he discovered. He had just been awarded the Nobel Prize.

If you were ever to win a Nobel Prize, it would probably change your life enormously, but Mr. Albert Einstein didn't care that he was famous. He had holes in the elbows of his sweaters, and his socks bagged around his ankles. My father called Mr. Einstein's shabby wardrobe his thinking clothes.

Mr. Albert Einstein came in November, when the days had cooled down enough for little boys and girls to sleep well at night, and thus we were put to bed early, perhaps before we were ready. That first night he told long stories to my parents after dinner, and the talk drifted down the hall to my room, where I lay awake, listening. I didn't know the words in the stories he told, but I understood the sadness in them.

Bad dreams. I woke up wanting to cry. Then I realized that a low, mournful weeping sound was already coming from the hallway. I rubbed my eyes, thinking someone had forgotten to turn off the shortwave radio.

But this curious weeping didn't come from the radio. Tiptoeing into the hall, I discovered that it came from the violin of Mr. Albert Einstein.

He sensed that someone was watching him play and turned around to face me. I saw his mouth, eyes, nose, and mustache crinkle together in a big smile, and I knew I would not be in trouble for getting out of bed so late at night.

He tried to speak to me in words, but I could not understand his language. So instead he played the violin, in short, enthusiastic bursts as though telling me something very exciting.

Music and mathematics are the same. He pulled the bow across the strings in a way I had never heard, and the sound made pictures in my head of the moon and the sunlight and my honored grandparents.

This is my latest mathematical equation. I scribbled it just today. The notes burst from his strings in a universal language. I envisioned a lush, green forest with a tiger running through the swaying grass and monkeys playing in the trees.

And now I'm going to have a little fun with relativity. There was an explosion of happiness and light, and the six o'clock commuter train vibrated, shook, jumped its tracks, and took off into the sky, dropping its passengers off on any star they chose.

Here is a man trying to catch a ray of light, and Mr. Albert Einstein played on and on and on.

In the morning I was back in my bed and didn't know how I'd gotten there.

The next night after dinner, as I lay tucked away in my bed, I again heard the adults talking and telling stories. Mr. Albert Einstein told wonderful jokes and made even my mother laugh. Later, when the rest of the house had gone to bed, he played his violin alone in his room—merry tunes, sweet, tangy sounds, the last thing I heard before I fell asleep.

My father asked his houseguest, "Why do you play your violin every night?"

"To clear my head so I can sleep," replied Mr. Albert Einstein.

During the day *Doctor* Einstein would lecture to Japanese scholars at a nearby university. One of these lectures would inspire a young physicist, Hideki Yukawa, who went on to win a Nobel Prize himself several years later.

Mr. Einstein returned from those lectures in a very good mood, for physics was one of his favorite subjects. Then he would pick up the little boy Basho Muramoto and bounce him on his knee. That little boy was *me.*

I do not remember when he left; I only remember the time he stayed with us. Many years passed. A war came to

Mr. Albert Einstein's country. A war came to my country. He moved to America and so, eventually, did I.

Mr. Albert Einstein arrived in Princeton, New Jersey, in 1933, his violin in hand. He was even more famous now and just as unconcerned about it as ever. He stopped wearing socks and started smoking a long pipe. Mr. Albert Einstein found New Jersey a good place to think about science. When he had a difficult mathematical problem to solve, he would pick up his violin and play for a while. Then he would stop suddenly, smile, and say, "Now I have it."

When he was not discovering new scientific theories, Mr. Albert Einstein continued to play his violin. And he always enjoyed making friends with children. Once on Halloween, a group of little girls went to his house, intending to play a prank on the famous scientist. But Mr. Einstein seemed to know when children were out to misbehave. When they arrived, he met them at the door with his violin. They probably expected to be spanked with his bow, but instead he proceeded to play. The girls felt ashamed that they had even considered bothering such a great and kind man.

Other children came to his house and asked for help with their arithmetic. There always seemed to be somebody on his doorstep, and then one day it was me.

I was a young man now and I was a little nervous when I knocked at 112 Mercer Street. What if Mr. Albert Einstein didn't remember me? I stood very straight and tall, and it was he who answered the door. I saw the familiar nose and mustache, the familiar wisp of white hair. He was also studying my face, and before I had a chance to introduce myself, Mr. Albert Einstein said, "I used to bounce you on my knee."

I did not come alone. I came with my violin, for Mr. Albert Einstein had inspired me, too.

We played our violins together often in those days, practicing Mozart and Beethoven in the Mercer Street house. Sometimes in between concertos, he would stop and look at me. "You play very well in time," he said.

And what is time? *Time*, said Albert Einstein, *is relative*.

Then we picked up where we had left off, and it was just as though we had never been apart. Because old friends can do that.

BIBLIOGRAPHY

Black Music in America: A History Through Its People by James Haskins. This book gives a panoramic view of African-American music and describes its influence on American culture.

Dragonsong by Anne McCaffrey. Menolly, who lives on the planet Pern, leaves the safety of Half-Circle Hold to pursue her love of music and to begin a new life. Discover what happens when she meets the fire lizards.

The Facts and Fictions of Minna Pratt by Patricia MacLachlan. A young cellist named Minna Pratt searches for her own personal technique or way of interpreting the music that she plays.

Giants of Jazz by Studs Terkel. This book features short biographies of some of jazz's greatest musicians.

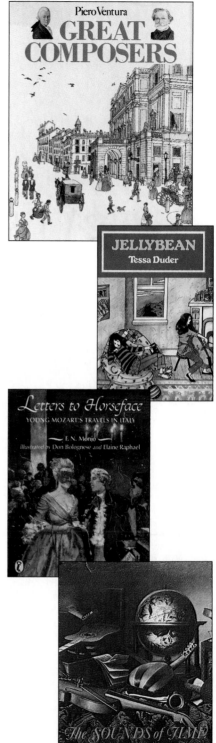

Great Composers by Piero Ventura. Ventura's book contains some fascinating information about the personalities and hardships of the world's great composers and tells how their lives influenced their work.

Jellybean by Tessa Duder. Geraldine wants nothing more than to become a great musical conductor. Find out what happens to her during a school performance of *The Nutcracker Suite*.

Letters to Horseface: Young Mozart's Travels in Italy by F. N. Monjo. In a series of letters to his sister, Nanerl, Wolfgang Amadeus Mozart gives details of his journey through Italy, where he is performing and composing music.

The Sounds of Time: Western Man and His Music by Nancy Wise Hess and Stephanie Grauman Wolf. This book is a history of music in the Western world, from the tenth century B.C. to the twentieth century A.D.

ANCIENT CIVILIZATIONS

DIGGING UP THE PAST

from DIGGING UP THE PAST: THE STORY OF
AN ARCHAEOLOGICAL ADVENTURE
by Carollyn James
illustrated by Pat and Robin DeWitt

Walking up the hill to his friend Joe's, Damien Shea
was thinking about Rocky Mountain sheep and
what he was going to do for the last three days of
spring break.

With one foot on the sidewalk and the other in the road,
Damien pretended he was a Rocky Mountain sheep climbing
up a rock slide. One false move, one loose rock, and he would
tumble off the mountain. He kept his eyes on his feet.

"Ah, ha!" he said. Next to his left shoe, poking out of the
leaves at the curb, was a quarter. Before putting it in his pocket along with the two large bolts, the pen, and the screwdriver he'd found since breakfast, Damien looked at the coin

closely. It was dated 1973. This quarter is older than I am, he said to himself, thinking it was better to spend it before it got any older.

Before seeing Joe, Damien bought gum at the 7-Eleven. He and Joe would need something to chew on while they explored the woods behind Joe's house.

Joe was lucky to have the town's park for a backyard. The park was all wooded, with a crayfish stream sandwiched between two hills. It was the kind of place two ten-year-olds like Damien and Joe could spend whole days exploring nature on their own. And they often did.

This particular day, Damien and Joe made another secret path to the fort they had made out of scrap pieces of wood a week ago. While they worked, they were on the lookout for anything curious. By sunset, their pockets were full of the day's finds.

Before dinner, Damien showed his mother his discoveries.

"The screwdriver's a little bent," Damien said, "but it'll still work."

"I like this rock," Mrs. Shea said. "Do you think those green veins might be gold?"

"Get real, Mom. It's just copper," he said.

Mrs. Shea held a small piece of blue glass up to the light. "Where did you find this?" she asked. The top was round and fluted, with a bubble of clear glass in the middle. As the light passed through it, the fluted points shone like an exploding star. "This is cobalt blue glass. It might be a hundred years old."

Damien told her he found it in the woods behind Joe's house.

"I think you found yourself an old perfume bottle stopper." She held the glass to her nose. "You can almost smell the perfume."

Damien told her that he found lots of old things in the woods. Last week he found a brown bottle with a medicine label.

"You know what," Mrs. Shea said, "you may have found an *archaeological site*."

Damien's mother was an archaeologist. Archaeology is the science of studying the life and culture of people of the past. Part of Damien's mother's work as an archaeologist was finding buried places where people had lived and worked hundreds, sometimes thousands, of years ago. She found many of these places, or sites, by carefully looking for archaeological clues lying on the ground's surface. The clues might be things people made long ago—things called artifacts—like a broken piece of a bowl or a nail or an arrowhead. Another clue might be an interesting way rocks are arranged, as if around a campfire. Like Damien, she had to be a keen observer.

"Wow, Mom!" Damien yelled. "You mean like I might have found an old Indian village or Egyptian tomb?"

"No. I mean like an old junkyard," said Damien's mother. "Often junk can tell archaeologists more than treasure can. A long time ago," his mother continued, "our town may have been a farm. It's hard to tell that now, with all the houses and streets and the interstate highway. But maybe what you found is evidence of what it used to be."

Damien slapped his thigh and thought, Well, I'll be doggoned. He wanted to find more clues about his town's past life.

"If we go into the woods as scientists," she told him, "we'll find a whole lot more than just neat stuff, Damien. We'll find out about the people who left all that neat stuff there. And maybe even *why* they left it there."

But his mother said she wouldn't help unless he promised that he was going to behave like an archaeologist. She explained that there are rules and methods archaeologists follow.

"Without rules," she said, "you destroy the meaning of everything you find and the things you'll find will have no meaning."

Damien nodded and promised he'd behave like a scientist.

"The first step in archaeology is to ask the right questions," his mother said. "All science is a way of looking for answers, Damien. What question do you think we should ask first?"

"Uh . . . why did the farmer dump his garbage in the woods?"

"We're too far ahead of ourselves. We still don't know for sure if there was a farm here. Right now we're simply asking, Did people live or work around here before this was a town? If we can find out that they did, our knowledge of archaeology will help us to ask more questions. Where did they come from? What was their life like? Why did they leave? We'll start looking for answers later. Right now, let's set the table."

After dinner, Damien and his mother went to the library. The town kept its special records at the library in acid-free folders and boxes that preserved the paper from rotting. The town's old photographs, original land deeds, subdivision and tax records, and maps were its history. These documents were like pictures in a family album. They were proof of how the town had grown and changed, and changed some more before it became the place where Damien lived today.

At the librarian's desk, Damien asked if he could see the town's historical documents. He told the librarian he was looking for an archaeological site in the woods, but first he needed to know if anyone used to live there.

The librarian left and came back with a box of old documents. Damien and his mother began to search through them. After a while, Damien found an old picture of Joe's house. It looked different. Instead of a garage, there was a barn, and the big oak in Joe's front yard was much smaller in the photograph.

"In 1867," the librarian told Damien, "a farmer named Matthew Abbott built that house on fifty-five acres of land. It was his grandson who sold the farm to the people who built our town."

In the photograph, the woods looked bigger.

"Damien," Mrs. Shea looked at the photograph, "I think this answers our first archaeological question. Now we're ready to ask another question."

"Right, Mom. What's for dessert?"

The next morning, Damien was over at Joe's before sunrise.

"Wake up!" Damien yelled up at Joe's bedroom window. "You're living in Matthew Abbott's house!"

Joe's father came to the window. "Damien," he said, "do you know what time it is?"

"Sure. Five, six o'clock," Damien said. "Did you know your house is more than a hundred years old?"

"Damien, go home. Now."

When Damien got home, he made his breakfast and read comic books until seven. Then he woke up his mother, who also asked him if he knew what time it was.

At nine o'clock, Damien called the mayor's office. The woods officially belonged to the town, and Damien had to get permission to work there. When the mayor said, "My dear little boy," Damien knew the mayor wasn't taking him seriously. The mayor said that he couldn't possibly give him permission because then every little boy in town would want to dig up the parks. Damien said that he didn't want to dig up the park. He wanted to excavate it!

"This is not a game, sir. Archaeology is a science!" Damien nearly shouted into the telephone.

Then Damien's mother got on the telephone. She told the mayor that as an archaeologist she would make sure that proper archaeological methods were followed in excavating the site if the town gave them permission. She apologized for her son calling him but said she would write him later that day to request permission.

"Today we want to go and surface collect, to make sure that a site exists. If you give us temporary permission," she told the mayor, "we'd like to start mapping it out. And, if there's time, we could start a test pit."

She promised that when they were finished digging and studying their findings, they would give whatever they found to the town. She also promised that they would fill in any holes they created. And she invited the mayor to come and watch.

The mayor said he might like to visit the site and that, yes, they had his permission, temporarily.

By this time Joe had come over to Damien's house, and Damien was talking real fast. Did Joe know there used to be a barn behind his house? That his house used to be a farm? Did he want to see a picture of it? Did he want to be an archaeologist?

Joe said, sure, he wouldn't mind being an archaeologist. But first he'd like to be a pitcher for the Orioles.

"Forget baseball, Joe," Damien said. "Starting today you're going to be an archaeologist."

With Mrs. Shea's help, the boys began collecting the tools they would need for their field kits to map out the site. Into

their backpacks they put pencils, markers, graph paper, balls of string, measuring tape, a compass, and a bunch of wooden stakes. "Aahhhgg, ze Count Dracula dies," Damien said, holding one of the stakes to his chest and pretending to faint on the couch.

"All those stakes are going to be useful," his mother said. "You'll need them for marking off the areas you'll be digging in." She added Band-Aids to their kits, and then gave each boy a mason's trowel. "Don't lose these. These trowels are your most important tools," she said.

They went into the garage for a couple of square shovels and the screen they would use to sift the dirt. The loose dirt would be put on top of a window screen table that they would shake back and forth, Damien's mother explained. "If there's something in the dirt we miss seeing when we dig, we'll shake it out with this."

After putting the trowels in their field kits, Joe and Damien carried them along with the screen down to the site. Damien's mother brought the shovels and the buckets.

"Before we begin," she asked, "what question do we try to answer now? What exactly are we looking for in the woods?"

"That's easy. Did Farmer Abbott dump his trash in the woods?" Damien said.

"Well, what you're really asking is, is there any evidence left of the Abbott family in the woods? Probably it will be their trash," she said.

They went across the street, down the block, and through Joe's backyard into the woods. Damien's mother asked where they had found the old medicine bottle and they showed her the spot near a small mound.

"And over there," Damien said, pointing to the right, about ten feet away, "is where I found the perfume stopper."

His mother pointed to a row of daffodils behind them. "How did daffodils get out here?" she asked. "And why do you think they're growing in a long, straight line like that?"

"Because someone planted them that way?" Damien said.

"That's possible," she said. "People often plant daffodils along fence lines. Perhaps the Abbotts did, too." Looking at the mound, and then looking up at Joe's house, Damien realized this looked like a good place to have a backyard fence . . . and a very good place to put a junk pile.

Walking in a line behind the flowers, Joe found a rotted wooden post sticking out of the ground. In the opposite direction, Damien found another. Walking back toward Joe, Damien stumbled over the stub of another post. It was an old fence line, all right.

"When we get back home," Mrs. Shea said, "I have to contact the state historical society, to let them know about this place. But for now, boys, let's start mapping."

"I don't see why we have to draw a map when we already know where the site is," Damien said.

"Because archaeology is about *where* you find things as much as it is about *what* you find," Mrs. Shea answered. "Without a map, nothing will have a place. And archaeologists map what they find vertically as well as horizontally. We're going to be working up and down as well as across. Trust me, we're going to need a record for that. But, like any map, we first need a name for this place."

They decided to call the site Matthew Abbott's Dump One, in case there might be more than one trash pile in the woods. Or "M.A.D. 1" for short.

That settled, they had to figure out where to begin their map. Damien's mother explained, "We can't just draw a map, willy nilly, because then the map could be of any place. We need what's called a datum point for this site. A datum point is something peculiar to this site, and permanent. It will be the map's reference point, the place that we measure everything else on the map from. That way, after we're finished digging, anyone who wants to know where our site was can use maps and our datum point to find it. Let's see . . . is there something around here we can use as a datum point?"

"The daffodils?" Damien asked. Mrs. Shea said that while the daffodils were very noticeable now, archaeologists needed something more permanent. Not only couldn't they find the daffodils in winter, but someone might pull them up.

"How about a tree?" Joe asked.

There was a big oak tree about 15 feet from the center of the mound. They decided to make the tree their datum point.

"Don't you think we should dress up our datum point?" Damien asked. "Like tie a red scarf around it or something?"

"How about tying my sister to it?" Joe laughed and Damien pretended he was Joe's sister begging to be untied.

Damien's mother had drawn a black dot in the middle of a piece of graph paper and marked it Large Oak Tree. "What we really need for our datum point are directions."

Damien took out the compass and stood under the tree. Walking around the tree, he pointed out north, south, east, and west. On the map, his mother drew four straight lines from the datum point. The map was now divided into four squares.

Avoiding the tree's roots, Damien pounded four stakes into the ground in a 10-foot square from the tree. On each stake he tied a long piece of string and gave the other end to Joe. Joe walked straight out from each stake. At the end of the string, he pounded another stake in the ground and tied the string to it. Now, north, south, east, and west were lined out from their datum point.

Working together, they began crisscrossing their string lines with more strings and stakes. First working along the north and south lines, they marked off every 5 feet with a stake. Then going along their east and west lines, they again staked out every five feet. Once the string was tied to their stakes, they had created eighteen squares, five feet by five feet.

"How come five feet, Mom?"

"The squares could have been any size, but I think five by five squares will give you enough room to sit down and work comfortably," she answered.

The squares went beyond where Damien had already found artifacts. But most of them were on and around the mound.

"These squares indicate where we will be digging," Mrs. Shea said. "If we need more squares, we can always make more."

On the map, Mrs. Shea marked off the squares just as they were laid on the ground. She made a note that each square was five by five feet, and then, inside of each mapped square, she wrote two letters and two numbers—using N, S, E, W and 1, 2, 3, 4.

The first letter in each square was an N or S. This meant the square was either north or south of the tree. The other letter was an E or W, for east or west of the tree. The numbers

told how close the square was to the tree, with the lowest numbers closest to it.

Each square had its own name, like a town on a map. Damien was standing in a square right on top of the mound. It was in the first row of squares south of the datum point and in the second row of squares west of the datum point. "What's this square called?" he asked. On his mother's map, this was square S1 W2. The square next to this one and right next to the tree was S1 W1. The square on the other side of Damien was called S1 W3.

"Archaeologists name each square for where it is from their datum point," Damien's mother explained. "Otherwise, it would take too long to figure out what square they were talking about. Okay, boys. Let's get ready to dig."

The datum point (tree) represents a 10-foot by 10-foot square.

"We need a test pit," said Mrs. Shea. "Let's dig it here." It was a square northeast of the tree, called N4 E3. The closest mapped square was N3 E2. "We can't expect to find any artifacts in this square, though."

"Then why dig it up?" Damien thought that was dumb. Who'd want to dig up a square with nothing in it?

"Because N4 E3 is going to teach us how to dig. And—more important—N4 E3 will help us compare the layers, or strata, of soil in the other squares to this one."

"I don't get it."

"Well, it's like comparing two dishes of ice cream. Let's say you have one dish with a scoop of vanilla and a little bit of chocolate sauce on top. And in another dish, you also have one scoop of vanilla and a little bit of chocolate, except that someone has mushed and mixed the sauce in with the ice cream. You only know what the mixed ice cream used to look like by looking at the first dish. . . . "

"You're making me hungry, Mom."

"The Abbots probably didn't dump their trash here, and probably didn't dig up any of the dirt here, either. So we'll learn what the natural ground looks like. This dirt is undisturbed, and it will let us know how much digging the Abbotts did. If they dug a hole to put their trash in, and then if they dug up more dirt to cover their trash, we'll know that because we'll compare it to how the layers of dirt look in this test pit."

The ground was covered with leaves. There were bits and pieces of old wet leaves stuck together under the dry leaves. Using her fingers, Damien's mother picked through the leaves and rubbed them. She found nothing. She piled them outside of the square. The boys did the same.

About an inch under the leaves, they hit dirt. They measured the depth of leaf covering. Damien's mother recorded it in their field notes. She wrote, "M.A.D. 1, N4 E3, leaf cover 0.0 ft–0.1 ft B.S." Then she wrote the date and her initials and showed it to Joe and Damien.

"Archaeologists always put their initials and date on everything they record," she told them. "That's so anyone who looks at their records will know who to talk to if they have any questions."

She told them that B.S. meant below the surface. "But why didn't you just write the leaves covered the square for about an inch?" Damien asked.

"As scientists," his mother said, "we're using scientific measurements and language. We change inches into decimals.

And leaf cover 0.0 ft–0.1 ft B.S. is the way archaeologists write down that the leaves did cover the square for about an inch. Now that we've drawn a map of the top of the site, from here on we'll be mapping the *depth* of the site. The very top of the site is 0.0 ft. From there, we measure down."

Once all the leaves were cleared from the square, Damien's mother showed the boys how to dig with a trowel. The flat side of the trowel was used to scrape the ground, a quarter of an inch at a time. "Never use the point to pry anything up," she said. "I can't stress that enough. If there is something in the ground too big to loosen by scraping, you scrape the dirt around it."

With the flat side of the trowel, the boys dug carefully, scooping the dirt into their buckets. Damien's mother used the square shovel the same way they used their trowels. When they had a bucketful of dirt from their square, they poured it over the processing screen. Joe and Damien took turns shaking the dirt through the screen.

"Mom! I think we found something!" Damien yelled every time they sifted the dirt. But the "something" always turned out to be just pebbles. Damien decided to save the rocks in a pile.

They dug carefully in N4 E3 all morning. By lunchtime, they had dug down two feet. It took a lot longer than they had thought it would. And as they dug, they noticed changes in the dirt. Under the leaves, the top layer of dirt was the blackest. This was the topsoil formed from years of plants and animals rotting on the ground. Below that was yellow clay. There was a band of sand under the clay. By late afternoon, they hit gravelly dirt.

5 feet

leaves

topsoil

clay

sand

gravelly dirt

Working together, it took them all day to dig down five feet. Damien's mother then took pictures of the square's walls. The different colors and textures of dirt made the walls look like waves of ribbons. It was starting to get dark, and everyone was hungry and tired.

"This is harder work than I thought, Damien," Joe said. "I think I'd rather pitch for the O's."

"Yeah," Damien agreed. "But think about how much better it will be when we find something."

"The mayor called last night," Damien's mother said. "He had good news. The City Council supports our dig."

For the rest of the site, they would dig each square in six-inch levels. Everything they found in one level would be recorded before they could begin digging up the next level. Each level of each square would have its own bag for artifacts.

Damien began digging in N1 W1 near the tree. Joe worked next to him in N1 E1. And Damien's mother took N1 W4.

"I bet I find more stuff than you, Joe," Damien said.

"Guys," Damien's mother said, "this is not a contest. We're all in this together. We're a team. We're here to find the Abbotts, not stuff."

"If we find the Abbotts, I'm out of here! Fast!" Damien said. As they started digging, the boys made jokes about finding old Abbott's bones.

In their first levels, they found only pebbles and roots. But soon after work began at the second level, Damien was jumping up and down at the processing screen.

"I got something! I got something!" he yelled.

He carefully picked the dirt off it with his fingers. It looked round and tinny, with something red written on it. Damien rubbed the tin hard against his pants.

He held it up to see if he could read it. "Coca-cola . . . Ah, it's just a dumb ol' bottle cap." Damien looked disappointed and started to throw it away.

"Hey, not so fast," his mother said. "When was the last time you had a Coke that wasn't a twist-off cap. Someone sat under this tree years ago and drank a Coke. It's an artifact. Put it in the bag. Everything interesting goes into the bags. When we get into the lab, then we'll decide what's important." The bottle cap went into the second-level paper bag marked, M.A.D. 1, N1 W1, 0.5–1.0 ft. B.S., Damien.

Joe found three cigarette filters and a piece of rusted tin in his second level. He put them in his second-level bag.

There was now a large pile of dirt under the processing screen from the first and second levels. Joe and Damien moved the dirt away to get ready for the third level. Damien's mother took pictures of the boys as they measured levels one and two in their squares.

As they worked level three, Damien's trowel hit something hard. He thought it was probably a rock, so he didn't get excited. As he scraped away the ground around it, though, he saw that it was white. Damien used a whisk broom to brush it clean. As more dirt fell off it, he spotted what looked like a set of teeth.

"Joe," he whispered. "Joe! I think I found Farmer Abbott."

Joe went over and looked. They both stared in silence at the jawbone in the dirt. They were so quiet that Damien's mother got suspicious. She went over and found the boys sitting perfectly still and looking at the ground.

"You boys look like you've seen a ghost," she said. Joe's mouth was open, but he wasn't saying a thing. He pointed to the jawbone jutting up at Damien's knees.

"May I?" she asked, and bent down and began carefully sweeping and troweling the area around the bone until it was

completely uncovered. She picked up the bone and studied it. She looked at the teeth and said, "What a pretty set of teeth."

"Mom, that's a disgusting thing to say about the dead!"

"Why? Whose teeth do you think these are?"

"Farmer Abbott's. I bet this is where he died."

"Damien, look at these teeth a little more carefully. Do these look like human teeth? Are they the same size and shape as your teeth? Count them. Hold the bone next to your chin. Do you think this bone came from a human being?" she asked.

Damien looked at it closely and said, "Maybe it came from a real ugly human. . . ."

"A sheep is more likely," his mother said. "We'll find out for sure later. But I'm glad you didn't pry it out of the ground. If you had, it might have broken."

In the notebook she wrote where the bone was found and who found it. Damien put the jawbone back exactly in its place in the pit. He measured how far down it was from the surface and how far it was from the pit's walls. His mother took a picture of it.

"Does anyone know if this jawbone is an artifact?" she asked them.

Both of them said it sure was.

"Why do you say that?"

They knew then it was the wrong answer.

"Did someone make this jawbone or use this jawbone? Just because we're saving it doesn't make it an artifact," Damien's mother said.

"It's not an artifact," Damien tried bluffing. "We meant to say it's a . . . it's a . . ."

". . . a bone!" Joe said for him.

"Archaeological sites have artifacts and non-artifacts," she said. "Artifacts are things people made or used. Non-artifacts are things people didn't make—like seeds, shells, and bones. But non-artifacts can tell us as much as artifacts about the people who made a site. What could this jawbone tell us about Farmer Abbott?"

"That he had a sheep," Joe said right away.

"And our job as archaeologists," she went on, "will be to find out why he had a sheep. Maybe sheep were pretty common on nineteenth-century farms. But, then again, maybe they weren't."

"Yeah. And we have to find out where he put the rest of the sheep," Joe said.

As Damien soon discovered, more of the sheep was buried in his third and fourth levels. Once the bones were measured and photographed in the square, they were bagged for the lab.

From the second level down, everyone was finding interesting things. Joe found the top part of a light blue jar. Damien's mom said it might have come from a canning jar.

Then Joe found more glass pieces of the same color. Damien's mother found the handle of a blue and white teacup and part of a leather strap.

As Joe was taking his dirt to the screen, a man came walking through the woods, waving his arms over his head.

"Hello! Are there any archaeologists out here?" he yelled from across the stream.

"It's the mayor. Be nice, Damien," Damien's mother said. She stood up, wiped her hands on her jeans, then crossed the stream to greet the mayor. Damien and Joe couldn't hear them, but they saw her pointing to them. The mayor started waving some more. The mayor and Damien's mother walked over to the site.

"So this is Damien," the mayor said. "It's a pleasure to meet such a nice little boy."

Damien shook the mayor's hand and introduced Joe. When the mayor said Joe was a nice little boy, too, Damien and Joe looked at each other and rolled their eyes.

Damien's mother explained how they were excavating the site and recording their findings. Then she asked the mayor if he'd like to watch Joe work the screen.

The mayor asked if he could try it. As he sifted Joe's dirt, he said this reminded him of helping his mother make cakes. He kept shaking the screen and talking about her triple-layer double-dutch chocolate cake that was as light as air. He paid little attention as the little rocks bounced on and off the screen. By Joe's account what happened next wasn't fair. It was Joe's dirt, after all.

After the dirt was shaken off, the screen held about a cup of small rocks. The mayor said, "My, my, that was fun. . . .

And what have we here?" He reached over and picked a small coin out of the rocks.

It was the size of a dime, the color of a dime, but it wasn't a dime. On one side was a woman's head with "United States of America" and "1874" written around it. On the other side was the Roman Numeral III. "I found a three-cent piece!" the mayor shouted. "I found a three-cent piece!"

Everyone but Joe was real excited. Damien's mother said this could help them date what they found in their third levels. Unless they found something with a different date on it, the levels 1.0 to 1.5 B.S. were buried around 1874. The mayor kept saying how lucky he was and how much fun archaeology was.

Damien said, "Three cents? Three cents? There's no such thing as a three-cent coin!"

To himself, Joe said that was his three-cent piece, that was his dirt—and that he wanted to go home.

The mayor turned to Damien's mother and told her, "The whole City Council will hear about this." He told her to let him know if they needed anything, anything at all. She thanked him and said they certainly would.

After the mayor left—Damien checked to make sure he left without the coin—Damien's mother went to talk with Joe.

She agreed that it didn't seem fair that the mayor found the coin. But, she told him, "Working a site is a lot like being on a baseball team. Everyone works for the same goal. Whether it's winning the game or digging the best site possible. And that coin did something very special for this site. Since the mayor thinks he found it, we now have the community's support. Thanks, Joe."

Joe felt better. And, anyway, the coin went into the bag marked with *his* name, not the mayor's.

It had been a long day, but time had passed fast. In less than eight hours they had dug into the nineteenth century.

THE
SEARCH
FOR EARLY
AMERICANS

from SEARCHES IN
THE AMERICAN DESERT
by Sheila Cowing

I n 1888, the Civil War had been over for twenty years. Thousands of eastern Americans had traveled west in covered wagons, looking for new land to farm, new homes, new ways of life. Roads and railroads were being built across the nation.

In the mountains and on the high desert plateaus, the frantic search for gold and silver was over, too. Most mines were run by big companies digging deep under the earth with heavy machinery.

On the plains, on grassy mountain slopes, and in the desert, wherever grass grew, new settlers drove cattle and sheep, searching constantly for fresh grass and water. The miners and the western settlers clashed with the native Americans. On the Great Plains, the Indians were forced to move onto reservations or to engage in war. In the Rocky Mountains, most native Americans had been killed or driven onto small, isolated reservations where many died of diseases they caught from the white man. Often the Indians found the land set aside for them already occupied by miners or settlers who refused to move. The native Americans were left impoverished and heartsick.

In the Mancos Valley of southern Colorado, which belonged traditionally to the Ute Indians, new ranchers herded their cattle out of the wide treeless valleys up steep, narrow canyons for the winter. There the animals were safe from the terrible icy winds and could be guarded more easily against wolves and mountain lions.

Richard Wetherill and his family had been raising cattle in Mancos for eight years. The Utes were not always friendly toward settlers. But Richard and his family, who were Quakers, had befriended them and had cared for several Indians when they were ill.

Richard was thirty years old, and he and his four younger brothers still lived with their parents. Their married sister lived close by.

Sometimes, during the winter, Richard and his brothers would build a small cabin so they could stay near the cattle. Then they would often ride into the branch canyons looking for ruined cliff dwellings. An old Ute had told them that in the canyons there were the abandoned dwellings of many people—the "ancient ones." One of the dwellings was larger than the others, and the Utes never went there, as it was a sacred place. Richard and his brothers had found only small dwellings.

On December 18, 1888, Richard and his sister's husband, Charlie Mason, rode to the top of Mesa Verde looking for stray cattle and found themselves in a place they had never been before. It was snowing lightly, and they rode close to the edges of the steep cliffs. Thick mesquite underbrush scratched their horses' legs and sometimes snared their hooves.

Late in the morning, they climbed down to rest the horses and walked out on a point of bare rock. Below them, a snowy canyon opened out. Suddenly, Richard grabbed Charlie's arm and pointed. About a half mile away, across the canyon, was a long, deep cave. Inside, blurred like a mirage in the falling snow, was a man-made wall. It was several stories high, with black window and door holes watching the canyon like eyes. Near the center rose a round, tapered tower.

Keeping their horses as close to the rim as they dared, they started around the canyon. Winding through prickly bushes, they reached a clearing. The cliff dropped away at their feet. Beneath them was the mysterious city in the canyon wall.

Richard climbed down from his horse. He took out his bowie knife and began to slice at the thick branch of a dead piñon tree.

They made a ladder, looping branches with their lariats, and tied it to piñon trunks. When they lowered the ladder over the cliff, it reached the ruins.

There stood a ghost city. This must be the large sacred dwelling the Ute had spoken of. Walls of the rooms had broken, but their remains stood straight, built of stone the red-brown color of oak leaves in winter. Little houses perched one on top of the other. The tower rose near the center, as though uniting the houses. At some point, Richard thought of the name "Cliff Palace" for this place, and the largest ruin at Mesa Verde is still called by that name.

For hours they explored, ducking through low doorways and climbing tumbled walls, searching room after room, leaving footprints in dust perhaps for centuries undisturbed. When they spoke to each other, their voices echoed.

Clay bowls, mugs, and jars for carrying water stood on ledges and floors as though their owners had just put them down and would come back soon to start supper. They found a stone axe, its handle still lashed to its blade. Hundreds of people must have lived here. What had happened to them?

In a back room, they found bones and three skulls. Had there been a battle? No, there would be many more skeletons.

Cliff Palace is the largest cliff dwelling in Mesa Verde National Park in southwestern Colorado. About 400 people lived there at one time.

Snow still fell on the mesa and the men were cold, but they were eager to learn whether other large ruins lay close by. Agreeing to camp near where they had first seen Cliff Palace, Richard and Charlie separated. In the late afternoon light, Richard rode north, then across Mesa Verde, following the curve of a deep canyon. There he saw another cliff dwelling rising in places to three stories. He dared not climb down, as it would soon be dark. The walls of this town were protected from the wind by a fringe of spruce trees across the front of the

Spruce Tree House, a prehistoric Anasazi dwelling in what is now Mesa Verde National Park, was discovered late one snowy afternoon in 1888 by Richard Wetherill, a cowboy who was so excited by his find that he devoted the rest of his life to archeological exploration.

cave. One tall spruce had grown right through a retaining wall. Richard called this ruin Spruce Tree House.

When morning came and Richard and Charlie tried to find Spruce Tree House again, they rode out to the edge of a different canyon. Curved in a hollow at the base of a cliff lay a third ancient village. It was smaller than Spruce Tree House, built around a square tower four stories high. This ruin they named Square Tower House.

Richard Wetherill and Charlie Mason were not the first to discover cliff dwellings in Mesa Verde. But what they found that December—Cliff Palace—belonged to a prehistoric civilization no one in the United States had dreamed of. Cliff Palace was an important clue in the mystery surrounding the ruins and the people who once had lived there. The towns these people left behind were preserved in the dry desert air. Richard Wetherill would devote the rest of his life to searching for their story. Charlie Mason would never lose interest in his brother-in-law's search although he moved with his family to Creede, Colorado, where he raised trout in a fish hatchery. Sometimes he even accompanied Richard on explorations.

Richard Wetherill knew that farther south in the open desert, scientists were trying to learn more about the native people who lived in walled adobe villages called pueblos. He felt sure that the Mesa Verde towns belonged to the ancestors of these people, although the walls and towers in the cliffs were more beautiful than any he had seen in pueblos. He wrote to the Smithsonian Institution in Washington, D.C., and the Peabody Museum at Harvard University in Massachusetts, telling them of his discovery. He hoped they would send their scientists to help, or at least sponsor him and his brothers, so that they could hire help for their cattle and be free to explore the canyon dwellings. Both institutions rejected Richard's appeal.

The Smithsonian suggested he ship the artifacts he had found to them. No one would come out to help. They said Richard was not a trained scientist and that he should stop disturbing archeological treasure.

But Richard could not stop. As soon as they moved the cattle out of the summer pasture, he and his brothers climbed back into Mancos Canyon. During the fifteen months after the discovery of Cliff Palace, the Wetherills found one hundred eighty-two large cliff dwellings and many smaller ones. They searched two hundred fifty miles of Mesa Verde's steep cliffs. Richard made maps, marking locations of cliff houses. He drew pictures and took photographs. The men picked up pots, clay figures, and sandals woven from fibers of the yucca plant's long leaves.

When spring came, Richard carried his collection in a ranch cart across the mountains over three hundred sixty miles to Denver, where he sold it to the Historical Society. People did not seem very interested. A few Denver tourists came to the Wetherill ranch to see a cliff dwelling. They told Richard that others thought he was looting graves.

But Baron Gustaf Nordenskiöld, a twenty-three-year-old Swedish archeologist and tourist, saw Richard's collection at the Historical Society and was eager to see more. It took him days to reach the ranch from Denver. First he took a mining train to Durango. Then he bounced all day in a small, rented horsecart, over thirty miles of twisting canyon roads to Mancos.

He arrived dirty and tired, but he was still excited. Would Richard allow him to help, he wondered.

It was June. Richard knew that he and his brother Al would be able to explore only a few more days before they would be needed to move the cattle down to the valley. But he was glad to have a scientist interested in his search at last.

They set up camp near an alkali spring below a nine-room cliff house Richard had visited only once before. Baron Nordenskiöld described the water's taste as "nauseous." Was this spring, polluted like many desert springs with soda and salt from the soil, the ancient villagers' only water?

The climb to the ruin was steep and slippery. Loaded with digging tools, they struggled through tangled mesquite and then up the open, stony slope.

They began digging inside the red, broken walls of a circular room. Richard found round rooms in most of the cliff dwellings. Many were dug underground, with firepits and stone benches around the walls. He knew that native people farther south used circular underground rooms for meetings of the tribes' religious clans. The Hopis called the rooms *kivas*.

As Richard, Al, and the baron dug, clouds of red dust clogged their mouths and noses. The three men soaked their bandannas in water and tied them around their faces to make breathing easier.

Richard's shovel scraped on something. He began to dig more slowly, so he wouldn't break anything. It was a piece of pottery, black and white like others he had found.

Quickly the baron stopped him. The baron squatted in the rubble and began to pick and scrape the crusted dirt with

In 1889, Baron Nordenskiöld, a Swedish archeologist, worked with
the Wetherill brothers excavating prehistoric cave dwellings at
Mesa Verde. Here, Richard Wetherill sits on a windowsill of a beautifully
made building now called Balcony House.

Gustaf Nordenskiöld/Mesa Verde Museum, Cortez, Colorado

a mason's trowel. Gently, patiently, he scraped until the pot
stood free. Then the baron picked it up as carefully as he
would a newborn baby. The pot had not a single crack.

From then on, Richard used a mason's trowel, too. This was
how an archeologist collected artifacts. He watched Nordenskiöld measure, take notes, and draw floor plans in each room,

marking locations of every pot, bone, or sandal they found. Richard wanted to learn everything he could about this organized way of searching ruins, called archeology.

All summer, while Richard and Al tended cattle, the baron explored other cliff dwellings with Richard and Al's younger brother, John, in the arm of Mancos Canyon the baron named Wetherill Mesa. The baron believed the caves had been inhabited for a long time. The walls and towers could not have been built in a few lifetimes. The people had no horses or machines to help them carry or shape the stones and mix the mortar. How long the construction had taken the baron had no way of knowing. How long ago the ruins had been abandoned he could only guess.

Near Spruce Tree House, he cut down the spruce growing through the wall. The tree would not have been allowed to push through the wall of a town people lived in. The baron counted the trunk's growth rings and decided Spruce Tree House must be at least one hundred sixty-two years old. He and Richard believed it was actually much older. They thought the cliff dwellings had been built and left before the Spanish arrived in the 1500s, as there were no white man's tools in any of the ruins.

At the Chicago World's Fair in 1893, Richard Wetherill helped represent Colorado. Fairgoers were amazed at his exhibit. It was hard to believe that at least two hundred years before the United States was a country, children in desert caves played inside three-story red and yellow apartment houses built around graceful, tapered towers. The World's Fair itself was a city of white buildings made to look like ancient

Greece and Rome. America did not really have an architectural style of its own. Even the idea of many-storied houses was very new.

Others, too, had been discovering the ancient towns in cliffs, on canyon floors, and in the open desert. At the fair, Richard saw photographs of a cliff dwelling near Grand Gulch, Utah, west of Mesa Verde. Seeing them made him long to explore again. Then he met the Hydes, two wealthy brothers who offered to pay him to explore. He was to give everything he found to the American Museum of Natural History in New York City.

At last Richard Wetherill had a chance to prove he could conduct a scientific search. Even though scientists would not come to help him, he wanted his work to meet their standards. Archeology was a new field, and Richard was determined to be accepted within its ranks. He began to plan. He planned a task for each member of his expedition. He planned exactly how he would describe each artifact he found.

Grand Gulch bends and twists for fifty miles, one of the wildest desert canyons in the country. Yet at one time, it must have been a cultural center, for perched high in the steep cliffs are eighty cliff dwellings. At that point the canyon is so narrow that Richard's pack burros could not pass between its walls. The expedition camped on the cracked white sand wash where once the river flowed among huge rocks shaped like toadstools and dwarves before it entered the canyon.

Each day Richard and his men, carrying heavy packs, climbed the cliffs to the caves on narrow rope-and-branch ladders. Right away, Richard noticed something strange. These people had not used the same articles as the people at Mesa Verde. Digging, he almost never heard the muffled click of his shovel striking pottery. There were not many pottery pieces. Instead, he began to turn up pieces of woven baskets.

Then he found a sandal, woven of yucca fibers like those at Mesa Verde, but much more beautifully. The toe end was round. Mesa Verde sandals were indented at the little toe. He found a spear-throwing stick archeologists called an *atlatl* and spear points, but no bows and arrows. Could these have been different people than those at Mesa Verde?

When he dug into the cave floor, Richard discovered a place where sand had been plastered in a wall around an egg-shaped hole. He knew that Navajos and Utes stored grain this way and began to dig out the hole more carefully, hoping to discover remains of ancient food. Instead, he uncovered a large, finely woven basket. He dug around it until he could lift it out. Underneath lay a man's body.

It was not a skeleton. It was a mummy, a body preserved for centuries by the desert sand's great dryness. With the utmost care, Richard lifted the body out of the hole and laid it on the cave's sand floor two feet above. He cut away the yucca cloth sack and opened the remains of a rabbit-fur blanket.

The man had died in agony. His black-haired head was thrown up and back. His knees were pulled up tightly. He clutched his belly with his right hand, gripping his wrist with the other hand. He had been slashed across his belly and the whole way across his back.

Someone had tried to sew the terrible wound with a one-eighth-inch-thick cord of black, braided human hair. It must have taken a long time to work a deer-bone awl back and forth through the man's flesh. The stitches in the shriveled, leathery skin were half an inch apart. This must have been the only way to try to stop the gushing blood.

Near the man, Richard found a pair of feet and legs cut off at the knees and a pair of hands and arms sliced at the elbows. The rest of the body was missing. There were seven other mummies buried close by, with spear points in their skulls or backbones.

These people had been killed in battle, Richard thought. Their relatives had buried them with care, wrapping each in rabbit fur or in a cloth woven of turkey feathers, and then in yucca-leaf cloth. They had covered each head with a fine new basket holding new sandals, seed jewelry, and stone knives with wooden handles for each to use in his or her new life.

Later Richard found nearly one hundred men, women, and children buried in graves hollowed out in cave floors near Grand Gulch. Most of their skulls had been crushed, or they had been killed with stone spears. In one skeleton, he found a huge, black volcanic glass blade pinning the hip bones together the way a skewer fastens a roasting turkey. How hard someone must have thrown that blade!

Sitting in the sand at the first burial site, Richard looked around at the low walls the cliff dwellers had built in this cave. These walls were not built as well as those in Mesa Verde. Here, there were no graceful towers or many-storied apartment houses. He had found the bodies buried two to five feet below the tumbled walls.

He picked up a piece of a clay pot. It was rough, and he could see the prints of the fingers that shaped it. There were no pots buried with the bodies he had found, not even broken pieces. The people in Grand Gulch had not used pots, even though pots were more efficient than baskets for carrying water and for cooking. Then Richard remembered something.

He and Baron Nordenskiöld had found pots in a trash mound south of a cliff dwelling in Mancos Canyon. They were gray and coiled, not at all strong and polished like the pots the cliff dwellers there had painted black on white with lightning designs. Perhaps, the baron had suggested, the gray pots belonged to an older race of people.

Richard was excited. The heads of these mummies were shaped differently than those of the Mesa Verde people, too. Mesa Verde skulls were short and broad. The baron told Richard that was because they flattened their babies' heads by strapping them to rigid cradleboards, not the padded ones modern native people used. Perhaps the people buried under these cliff dwellings in Grand Gulch belonged to an entirely different, older race of people than the cliff dwellers who had last lived in these caves. Perhaps the original inhabitants of Grand Gulch had been killed by invaders who wanted to use the caves. Possibly the new people built the walls and made the first pots, pressing river mud around baskets to make the baskets hold water longer.

Richard called the older race the Basket Makers. He sent his field notes to the American Museum of Natural History in New York with the mummies and their sandals and baskets. He did not write well, but a scientist friend wrote an article in *Harper's Monthly*, a popular magazine, using the notes and the photographs.

Other scientists did not believe Richard. Because he had no scientific training, they insisted he was a fraud. At Harvard University, an archeology professor told his students that Richard had invented a new people in order to sell more artifacts. This criticism did not deter Richard. He kept on exploring, because he was so fascinated he couldn't stop. He loved exploring more than anything else.

During the summer of 1895, Mr. and Mrs. Sidney Palmer and their three children, Marietta, Edna, and LaVern, set up camp near Richard's ranch. Richard showed them the cave dwellings at Mesa Verde. That fall, Richard and the Palmers traveled south one hundred fifty miles to see a big ruin they'd heard about called Pueblo Bonito, in the Navajo reservation in northern New Mexico.

For six days they followed a wheel-rut road. The desert was high and flat with no trees and little grass, and the wind blew constantly. The wagon wheels slipped and dragged in the sand.

When the road turned east through a wide canyon wash where once the Chaco River had flowed, they rode past the ruins of a small pueblo. Soon they saw more tumbled walls. Then, to their left, curved against the dark sandstone mesa, lay a ruin that was larger than anything Richard had ever imagined.

Behind the ruin, he found holes in the cliff face, stairs the ancient pueblo dwellers had chipped with stone tools. Climbing, he stepped out on the mesa top overlooking the wide canyon.

Below him, Pueblo Bonito glowed red in the afternoon sun, spread out like a huge half-moon. The whole of Mesa Verde's Cliff Palace would be lost in one small section.

But that was not all. To the east he could see another great ruin. Across Chaco Canyon he could see mounds where several smaller pueblos might be buried. He might be looking down on an enormous city-state, like Rome or Athens!

Why had this civilization died? Where had all its people gone?

With Mr. Palmer, Richard rode across the northern mesa looking for Navajos who might have some of the answers. In the smoky light of hogans Wetherill spoke to the Navajos in their own language. The older Indian men all gave him the same answer. The great walls looked exactly the same as they had many generations before, when the Navajos first came to

Pueblo Bonito, in Chaco Canyon, was the largest ruin Richard
Wetherill had ever seen. In A.D. 1100, Chaco Canyon was the hub
of a major Anasazi complex of towns connected by hand-built roads.
In 1988, it was named a prehistoric archeological site of world importance.

Dick George/Tom Stack & Associates

the area. At that time more cedar trees and more grass grew on the mesa. The Chaco Wash had water in it and the stream flowed at the surface of the canyon floor, not far down between the eroded banks of an arroyo. But the ancient ones were gone, and no one knew who they were. *Anasazi*, the people called them, which meant "ancient enemy."

Richard and the Palmers explored for a month. They found eleven large pueblos with over one hundred rooms each, and more than one hundred smaller pueblos. Pueblo Bonito alone had more than six hundred rooms. It covered three acres and in some places rose five stories tall.

After they returned to Mancos, Richard could not stop thinking about Chaco Canyon. At one time thousands of people must have lived there. Could the Navajos, poor, wandering sheepherders, have destroyed so great a city? He did not think so. He knew that answers must lie beneath the piles of rubble inside the walls.

Soon after their visit to Chaco, Richard married Marietta Palmer. They tried to settle down to ranch life, but Richard was too restless. He was so fascinated with the Anasazi that he decided to move to Chaco Canyon. He and Marietta opened a trading post for the Navajos, which Richard hoped would support his family.

The Hyde brothers, who had helped finance the Grand Gulch exploration, agreed to send Richard money to excavate in Chaco Canyon. Richard would again give what he found to the American Museum of Natural History in New York City. The first organized search in Chaco Canyon began in 1896.

Over the next four years, Richard dug out nearly two hundred rooms in Pueblo Bonito. Soon he realized that this pueblo had been built differently than those at Mesa Verde. There, rooms were built as people moved in, with the beautiful towers added. But this huge, horseshoe-shaped pueblo had been designed ahead of time to meet a society's needs.

Some rooms were built of thin, flat rocks, others of large stones and mortar. Such different building methods suggested that the rooms had been built at different times and over many years. Walls in Pueblo Bonito lay twelve feet, or two stories, below the level of the main court and rose five stories above.

Rooms were laid over rooms, with huge pine timber ceilings between. The pine trees grew thirty miles away from the canyon. Traveling by foot, how long had it taken these people to haul pine trunks—thousands of them—to Pueblo Bonito? Construction of the pueblo must have taken a long time.

Richard had no way of knowing how long, or when the pueblo had been started. Years later another searcher, A. E. Douglass, discovered a way to find out. He counted the annual growth rings in the ceiling timbers just as Baron Nordenskiöld had done with the tree at Spruce Tree House. Then he compared those rings to many other pine timbers. Pueblo Bonito, he discovered, was begun around A.D. 950. That was five hundred fifty years before Columbus discovered America. Douglass decided that people had lived in Pueblo Bonito until after A.D. 1300. The Mesa Verde cliff dwellings were built later than the main section of Pueblo Bonito and were inhabited a shorter time.

Without measuring instruments, the Anasazi constructed
doorways of the same dimensions between Pueblo Bonito's many rooms.

© Spencer Swanger/Tom Stack & Associates

How could people have grown enough food in the open, hot desert for so long with so little rain? The Chaco River bed was hard, dry sand. When he was digging, Richard found only bitter springs.

Then, in July, it rained almost every day for two weeks. Walls of muddy water swept the wash, flooding ditches that Richard hadn't noticed. On the mesas, rainwater channeled into streams that fell over cliffs into shaded rock pools.

Recent research suggests that the Chaco River once flowed in the wash, flooding its banks each spring the way the Nile River did, watering Egyptian crops in ancient times. Did more rain fall in Anasazi times? Did the cliff pools store enough water for drinking and washing all year around? No one knows. People are still searching for answers in Chaco Canyon.

Not only could the Anasazi feed thousands in desert soil, but they also had time to build the largest city in the desert and to become master artists. Richard found pottery and jewelry more beautiful than any he had ever seen. He found hundreds of jars, many like those he'd found at Mesa Verde, but others painted with intricate designs or encrusted with chunks of turquoise. He found necklaces, pendants, bracelets, and carvings, many inlaid with turquoise or made of abalone shell, which shimmered like pearl in the sunlight.

The nearest turquoise mines were two hundred miles away. The nearest abalone lived in the ocean along the California coast, nearly one thousand miles away. Then Richard found the skeletons of fourteen macaws, large parrots with blue, red, yellow, or green feathers. Parrots live in the western Mexican highlands. These people must have traveled great distances!

Richard Wetherill, excavating Pueblo Bonito in Chaco Canyon for the Hyde brothers in 1897, found pottery and baskets at this site.

Perhaps some of these people had moved to Chaco from the cliff houses at Mesa Verde, but Richard knew now that at Chaco the culture was much more advanced. High on the mesas north and west of Chaco were other ruins that looked similar. Could they have been part of Chaco?

Chaco Canyon was a great center, as Richard had suspected. When modern archeologists looked down on the canyon from the air, they discovered that it was connected to at least seventy-five outlying towns by almost five hundred miles of straight roads. Even though they had no wagons or cars, so many people traveled that the Anasazi dug roads thirty feet wide. In some places, low walls or ledges can still be seen edging the road's shallow depression.

Chaco has been called the greatest archeological ruin north of Mexico. An estimated five thousand people lived in four hundred settlements in and around the canyon, dependent on food grown in desert soil. These prehistoric people developed new building techniques. They watched the seasons change with a kind of solar observatory only recently discovered. They were skilled artists. They traded with people over a thousand miles away.

Why did they leave Chaco? Where did they go? Richard found no evidence of terrible battles as he had at Grand

In 1897, Navajo Indians helped Richard Wetherill dig in Pueblo Bonito.
American Museum of Natural History

Gulch. Later searchers believe that groups of people moved all over the desert, as Mesa Verde people had moved into Chaco Canyon. They probably moved in search of water.

When the trees in the forest thirty miles away were cut for ceiling timbers, the underground water those roots drew to the surface may have sunk. Then when the seasonal rains fell, the thirsty desert absorbed the water too fast for the people to catch and store it. The Chaco people, archeologists believe, wandered east to the Rio Grande, where the river flowed all year around, or south to Acoma and Zuñi, or west to Oraibi, home of the Hopis.

All over the southwestern desert, searchers have found abandoned cliff and mesa houses. Some are still unexplored, their floors littered with miniature corn cobs and shards of pottery. Since the ancient ones had no written language, people are still searching for clues to their history.

In the open desert south of Phoenix, Arizona, an ancient people archeologists call the Hohokam, ancestors of the Pima and the Papago, played an Aztec ball game in walled courts. They used a process of etching with acid cactus sap to decorate seashells, five hundred years before European artists "discovered" the method. The Hohokam did not build great adobe or stone cities.

Another ancient people, the Mogollon Mimbres in southwest New Mexico, were the first Americans to decorate pottery with animal, bird, and geometric designs. Their artistic abilities were unknown for centuries because they drilled holes in their pots and jugs and buried them with their dead.

In 1910, Richard Wetherill was shot and killed by a Navajo man, after an argument over a horse. Richard was fifty-two years old. Seven years earlier, archeologists, insisting that he was vandalizing Pueblo Bonito, convinced the federal government to stop his search. For many years, his collection lay in a storeroom at the American Museum of Natural History in New York City. In the summer of 1987, however, the results of Richard Wetherill's searches, the artifacts of the Hyde Expeditions, were displayed in a show at the museum.

Because Richard had no training, scientists did not afford him the recognition he deserved. But Richard's search laid a cornerstone for the science that became American Southwestern archeology. In 1914, when Alfred Kidder and S. J. Guernsey discovered in northeastern Arizona the same kind of remains that Richard had described at Grand Gulch, archeologists acknowledged Richard's discovery of the Basket Maker civilization. Another archeologist, John C. McGregor, pointed out in his book that when Richard dug beneath the cliff dwellers' floor and concluded that the graves were those of an older people, he was the first to use the principle of stratigraphy, which teaches that what is buried deeper is older. Above all, Richard is remembered as one of the first Americans to prove that a great civilization existed in the desert long before Europeans settled there.

THE ISLAND OF BULLS

from LOST CITIES by Roy A. Gallant

ccording to a Greek myth going back more than 2,500 years, there once was a young man named Theseus, son of the king of the great city of Athens, the capital of Greece. At this time there also lived on the nearby island of Crete a king named Minos. Minos was so powerful and so greatly feared that he was able to demand and get whatever he wished, not only from the people of his island-state but also from the people of nearby Athens on the Greek mainland.

Now it happened, according to the myth, that Minos kept on Crete a fierce monster called the Minotaur, a beast that was half bull and half man and ate human flesh. The word "minotaur" is built out of two words—King Minos's name and the Greek word *tauros*, meaning "bull." The Minotaur was supposedly kept in a labyrinth, a great maze or place of numerous winding corridors that was so complex that it was impossible to find the way out without help.

From time to time, Minos demanded that the king of Athens send him the seven handsomest young men and the seven most beautiful maidens of the land. These fourteen youths were then led into the labyrinth, where one by one they were found and devoured by the Minotaur.

When Theseus came of age he told his father that he wanted to be one of the youths sent to King Minos so that he might slay the Minotaur and once and for all end this terrible sacrifice the people of Athens were forced to make. Although he feared that his son would never return, Theseus's father granted the young man his wish.

On the appointed day the fourteen youths boarded the ship to Crete, a ship that always flew black sails, a sign of the certain death awaiting its passengers. When they arrived the youths were paraded before King Minos, for him to judge whether all were fair enough for the Minotaur. When the king's daughter, Ariadne, saw Theseus, she fell in love with him. She then managed to see him alone before the youths were led off to the labyrinth. Ariadne told Theseus of her love and gave him a small sword and a ball of thread.

As Theseus led the way into the maze he carefully unwound the ball of thread. On hearing the ferocious roars of the Minotaur as it came charging around a corner of the labyrinth to attack him, Theseus dropped the ball of thread and began slashing at the beast with the sword given to him by Ariadne. He managed to weaken the Minotaur and finally cut off its head. He then picked up the thread and followed it out of the labyrinth, leading his thirteen companions to safety and home.

Before he had departed from Athens, Theseus had agreed to change the black sails to white if all had gone well and he had slain the Minotaur. He forgot to do so. When his father, waiting for the ship's return, saw the black sails, he presumed that his son had been killed. He was so stricken with grief that he killed himself before the ship docked. Theseus then became king.

Was there any truth to the account of Minos and his kingdom on the island of Crete? The Greek poet Homer, who lived about 850 B.C., gave us the first known account of the Cretan king Minos and his palace. Later, in 455 B.C., the Greek scholar Thucydides, who lived in Athens, wrote an account of King Minos and his powerful fleet of ships that ruled the Aegean Sea. Still later, the philosopher Aristotle, born in 384 B.C., also wrote of King Minos dominating the whole Aegean area. And there were some who thought that Crete might have been the legendary kingdom of Atlantis, mentioned by the philosopher Plato about 400 B.C.

So Crete must have had a long history, one that stretched back even before Greek scholars wrote about the land. Crete itself did not have a written history until about 2,500 years ago. Even then the Minoans left very little in writing, unlike the neighboring civilizations of Egypt and Babylonia. The Cretans were called Minoans after King Minos. The legend of King Minos and his Minotaur had existed for centuries before the Minoans used writing. It had been handed down orally in story form from one generation to the next. But because it was only a legend, no one could be certain that there had actually ever been such a kingdom.

Fascinated by the Minotaur legend and poetic accounts of a highly developed civilization much older than any other known European civilization, an English scholar from Oxford University named Sir Arthur Evans decided to find out if there was any truth to the Minotaur legend and other accounts of an ancient Cretan civilization. The Minoans had ruled supreme from about 3000 to 1450 B.C., although as a civilization they were still older. The Minoan population at its peak was about 80,000, slightly less than the present population of Portland, Maine.

Evans's interest in Crete began during a visit to Athens where he bought a few moonstones from a Greek merchant. The stones, worn by his wife as lucky charms, had strange writing scratched on them. It was the writing that led Evans to Crete in 1894, where he found more of the stones containing the same writing. He first went to the capital of the island, Knossos, where he noted that many of the women were wearing similar round stones of clay around their necks or wrists as lucky charms. Although some of the stones had simple designs carved on them, others had what appeared to be some form of writing. As he traveled around Crete, Evans saw many such stones. They turned out to be very old indeed, and some had been used as personal identity disks by the ancient Cretans. One such stone had the design of a labyrinth. Another had the shape of a creature half human and half bull.

While in Knossos, Evans became curious about several large blocks of carved stone lying about. He decided to dig a few test trenches near the stones to see if anything might lie buried below. Only a few inches beneath the surface one of his thirty workers struck something hard with a spade. Evans's excitement grew as they continued to dig around the hard object. After only a few hours of digging Evans was almost certain that he had stumbled onto the walls of a large and ancient building, possibly the palace of the mighty Minos. In all, he spent more than twenty-five years working in Crete reconstructing the Minoan remains at Knossos. The hard object just beneath the surface indeed turned out to be the palace of King Minos, built some 3,500 years earlier, even earlier than the time of the great rulers of ancient Egypt just across the sea to the south.

In his search for Crete's past, Evans came across several seals. The one at left represents the legendary labyrinth. The seal at right shows an athlete leaping over a bull's back.

Ronald Sheridan's Photo Library

Month after month, year after year, the work continued. The palace of Minos turned out to be enormous, sprawling over an area larger than ten city blocks. It was shaped like a large rectangle, in the center of which was a huge courtyard of red cement. Some sections of the building were five stories high. There were twisting corridors and stairways. There were dead-end passageways and a bewildering number of rooms. Indeed, it was a labyrinth. Evans had no doubt that here was the building described in legend as both the home of Minos and of the dreaded Minotaur.

There was great excitement when the workers uncovered the first fresco. Frescoes are paintings done on walls when the walls are being plastered. In this way the plaster and the colors of the painting dry together, a process that preserves the paintings for a long time. One such fresco was a life-size painting of a young man holding a large cone-shaped cup. His skin was a deep reddish color from exposure to the sun. Other frescoes showed Minoan women, who spent most of the time indoors, as white-skinned. Throughout the palace were images of a two-bladed axe, a symbol associated with the Cretan mother-goddess, whom the Greeks called Rhea. At will she was able to enter the double-axe and vanish. An ancient word for this axe was *labrys*, from which the word labyrinth comes.

As the digging continued, Evans realized that the enormous palace had not all been built at the same time. Hallways, rooms, and storage areas were added on century after century. Minos seems to have been the name of the first Cretan king who constructed the original palace. In his honor, each of the future kings of Crete took the name of Minos and added to the palace to suit his own taste. Evans discovered large storerooms with great jars for wine and olive oil. Some of the jars stood as tall as a man and can be seen in place today. There were also containers lined with stone and with fragments of gold leaf. These were probably from the rooms where the Minoan kings kept their stores of gold, silver, and other precious metals. Nearby were apartments for the royal guards who kept watch over the king's wealth.

Evans again became excited when his workers uncovered what is probably the oldest known royal throne. As described by Evans, there "was a short bench, like that of the outer chamber, and then, separated from it by a small interval, a separate seat of honour or throne. It had a high back, like the

A ground plan reconstruction of the late Minoan palace at Knossos reveals a labyrinth of passageways and hundreds of rooms.

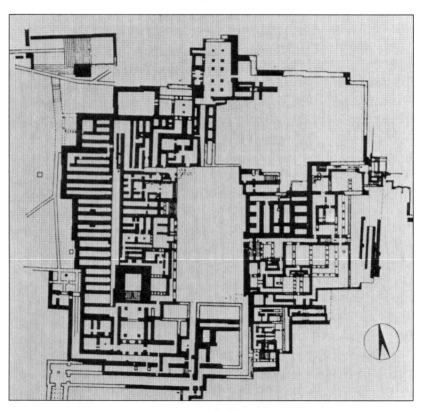

seat, of gypsum, which was partly imbedded in the stucco of the wall. It was raised on a square base and had a curious moulding below . . . probably painted to harmonize with the fresco at its side."

As the weeks and months passed, many more discoveries were made—the paved courtyard mentioned earlier, stairways with frescoes of olive branches in flower, a wall painting of a monkey gathering flowers in baskets, and a large fresco of a bull with young acrobats. Paintings and impressions of bulls on vases and other objects were so common that it caused Evans to remark: "What a part these creatures play here!"

Like the people of Spain today, the ancient Minoans seem to have loved a sport involving acrobats and bulls. One large fresco shows a bull in full charge and three young acrobats, two girls and a boy. If we read these frescoes correctly, some sport like this may have taken place: Three youths entered a sports arena containing a bull. As the bull charged, one of the youths would grab the animal's horns, leap over the bull's head, and do a handspring off the bull's back, landing upright on his feet and in the arms of one of the other two youths. This sounds like an impossible trick, but so many Cretan artifacts suggest that some such event took place that it is hard to doubt. Is it possible that this type of event inspired the myth of the fourteen Athenian youths, King Minos, and the deadly Minotaur?

There are frescoes that also show audiences watching the contests in the bull ring. Although in Spain the object of the cruel contest is to kill the bull by plunging a sword into it, in ancient Crete the purpose seemed to be to demonstrate the

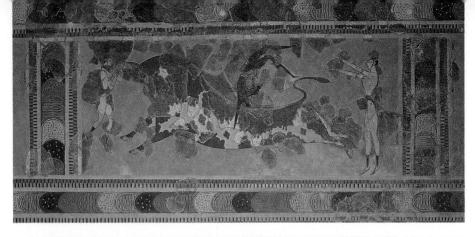

Wall paintings like this one at Knossos suggest that the Minoans loved
a sport in which acrobats vaulted over the horns and backs of bulls.

athletic skills of the acrobats. But surely, from time to time,
some of the youths must have been killed during the contests.

With a navy second to none, the Minoan kings ruled the
seas. They were wealthy, as suggested by an elaborate game
table Evans found, set with crystal, ivory, and gold and silver
pieces. And they were enlightened, as evidenced by the modern system of plumbing unearthed at Knossos. Enormous clay
pipes, some large enough for a person to stand up in, carried
water and sewage away from the palace. There also was a
system of pipes for hot and cold water flowing through the
palace. After four thousand years, the drainage system at
Knossos is still in working order. Nothing equal to it was built
in all of Europe until the mid-1800s. Since Evans's time at
least three other palaces have been found in other parts of the
island, some with as many as 1,500 rooms.

Who were the Minoans, and what happened to bring their
splendid civilization down? What they left behind shows
them as a people of uncommon grace and elegance who
reached an astonishingly high level of craftsmanship. Their

vases and bowls of stone and their finely carved gems were unmatched anywhere. And they were apparently a peace-loving people; they had no defense fortifications and none of their art shows scenes of battle, warriors, or weapons, although finely made real weapons of bronze have been found.

Their wealth most likely came from overseas trade. Elegant pottery made by them, and copied by other people, has been unearthed in Egypt, in the Near East, on the Aegean Islands, and in Greece. For many centuries the Minoans enjoyed the good life, but then their civilization collapsed and quickly disappeared.

About the year 1450 B.C. Knossos and other Minoan centers burned. By about 1400 B.C. these cities were completely destroyed. While some scholars have supposed that invaders swept over the island and conquered it, others doubt that this is what happened. They suspect that the catastrophic explosion of the volcanic island of Thera (also called Santorin), 60 miles north of Crete, sent the Minoans and their splendid civilization into oblivion.

MEET ROY A. GALLANT, AUTHOR

Roy Gallant has been writing ever since he was about fourteen years old, and today he is considered one of America's foremost science writers. "I'm in love with my work of science writing and would be lost without it. No matter what I may be writing at the moment—a book about fossils, a magazine article about the formation of limestone caves, or an occasional short story—I'm happy working out the problems of putting it all down so that others may learn something they did not know before. I often think that what I like best about writing is that I am educating people." Gallant enjoys the role of educator, whether he is writing a book on his word processor or lecturing to a classroom of college students.

THE PEOPLE ON THE BEACH

from THE SECRETS OF VESUVIUS
by Sara C. Bisel
*illustrated by Ken Marschall, Laurie
McGaw, Jack McMaster, Margo Stahl*

ATHENS, GREECE, JUNE 1982

he telegram lying at my door was marked "Urgent." As I bent down to pick it up, I hoped that it wasn't bad news. After spending a long hot day on my knees in the dusty ruins of an ancient Greek town, I was in no mood for surprises. When I ripped open the envelope I saw that it was from the National Geographic Society in Washington, D.C. They wanted me to telephone them immediately about a special project.

Why are they in such a hurry, I asked myself. As an archaeologist and anthropologist I have been involved in many expeditions. But my jobs are almost never emergencies. If something has been lying in the ground for a few thousand years, another week or two usually doesn't make much difference.

As I shut the door to my tiny apartment, I calculated the time difference between Athens, Greece, and Washington, D.C., and then dialed the long-distance number. My contact at the National Geographic Society wondered if I could spare a few days to examine some human skeletons that had just been found at the town of Herculaneum in Italy. Skeletons in Herculaneum, I thought to myself. Now *that* would be interesting!

Human bones are my specialty. In fact, I'm often called "the bone lady" because most of my work involves examining and reconstructing old skeletons. Believe it or not, bones are fascinating. They can tell you a great deal about someone, even if the person has been dead for thousands of years.

My job is to excavate and study the bones of people who lived and died many centuries ago.

© Jonathan Blair/Woodfin Camp & Associates

I can examine a skeleton and find out whether a person was male or female. If she was female, for example, I can tell you about how old she was when she died, whether she had children, what kind of work she might have done and what kind of food she ate. I can even glue dozens of small pieces of a skull back together like a jigsaw puzzle and show you what that person looked like.

The editor at *National Geographic* explained that workmen digging a drainage ditch near the ruins of Herculaneum had accidentally discovered some skeletons lying on what had once been the town's beachfront. Nearby, archaeologists had later uncovered some boat storage

I point out the different parts of a human skull to a group of young
anthropology students.

chambers in the ancient seawall. Much to their surprise, there
were more skeletons inside these cave-like rooms. Here people had found shelter from the terrifying eruption of Mount
Vesuvius in A.D. 79. As they lay huddled together in the dark,
they were smothered by an enormous surge of scorching gas
and ash from the volcano. Flowing hot ash, rock and pumice
then buried them. Today, almost two thousand years later, the
tangled remains of these ancient Romans lie as they fell, preserved in the wet volcanic earth.

This was an amazing discovery. Although archaeologists
have been digging out Herculaneum for centuries, very few
bodies had ever been found. As a result, experts had decided
that almost all of the Herculaneans must have escaped before
the disaster. We now knew that this was not true.

But even more exciting for me was the chance to study the actual skeletons of real ancient Romans. Because the Romans cremated their dead, they left behind plenty of urns full of human ashes but very few complete remains. So these Herculaneans represented the first large group of Roman skeletons ever found.

"I'll book a seat on the next flight to Naples," I said to the *National Geographic* editor and then slammed the receiver down. I quickly rolled up a few T-shirts and several pairs of jeans and stuffed them into my bag. I knew that I had to leave for Italy right away. Now that the skeletons had been exposed to the air, they had to be properly preserved as soon as possible or they would quickly disintegrate and turn to dust. If that was allowed to happen, a priceless opportunity to find out exactly what the ancient Romans had looked like and how they had lived would be lost.

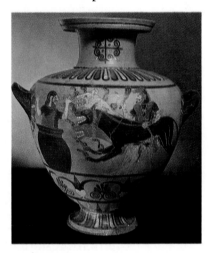

It was strange, I thought grimly, that Vesuvius, the volcano that had caused one of the biggest natural disasters in the world, was now giving me the most exciting assignment any physical anthropologist could ever dream of. I would be the first person to recreate the lives of these men, women and children who had lived and died so long ago. I knew that bones could talk. If I listened carefully, they would whisper their secrets.

The town of Herculaneum is named after the legendary strongman Hercules. This vase shows Hercules striking Cerebus, the three-headed dog.

Giraudon/Art Resource

What would these skeletons tell me?

. . . darkness fell, not the dark of a moonless or cloudy night, but as if the lamp had been put out in a closed room. You could hear the shrieks of women, the wailing of infants, and the shouting of men; some were calling their parents, others their children or their wives, trying to recognize them by their voices. People bewailed their own fate or that of their relatives, and there were some who prayed for death in their terror of dying. Many sought the aid of the gods, but still more imagined there were no gods left, and that the universe was plunged into eternal darkness for evermore.

Pliny the Younger
1st century A.D.

I put down my fork and reread the words that described a group of people trying to escape from the fury of Vesuvius on that August day so many years ago. A chill crept up my neck. I was no longer hungry.

I had been hoping to start examining the new skeletons soon after I arrived. But it was late by the time I checked into my hotel, and I knew that not much could be done until morning. You need good light for excavation work. So I'd had a bath, tucked a few books under my arm and gone down to the hotel restaurant where I ordered a plate of pasta. Then I settled down for a crash review lesson on ancient Hercula-neum and how the sudden eruption of Vesuvius had changed its fate forever.

The descriptions I was reading had been written by Pliny, a seventeen-year-old student who lived in Misenum, across the Bay of Naples. His uncle had sailed across the bay toward

Herculaneum to try to help stranded friends, until his ship was cut off by "bits of pumice and blackened stones, charred and cracked by the flames." Did Pliny's uncle have any idea what he was sailing into, I wondered. Or, when he saw from afar the mountain explode and a column of ash and smoke rise twelve miles into the air, could he simply not believe his eyes until he had taken a closer look?

Pliny's uncle eventually landed at Stabiae, several miles south of Herculaneum. Though "great sheets of flame" were flashing out from the peak of Vesuvius, he actually had a bath and went to sleep. But the people with him sat up in terror all night, while the buildings shook as if they were being torn out of the ground. When the door to the uncle's room became choked by a layer of cinder and ash, they woke him up and fled, tying pillows on their heads as protection against the pumice stones that rained around them.

But Vesuvius eventually caught up with Pliny's uncle. In spite of his calm bravery, he was suffocated by sulphur fumes while trying to get back to his ship.

Sulphur fumes caused by the eruption of Mount Vesuvius overcome Pliny's uncle in this painting done in 1813.

Musée des Augustins, Toulouse, France

Meanwhile, about twenty miles across the bay at Misenum, Pliny observed the various stages of the eruption, beginning with the appearance of the mushroom-shaped cloud of ash, followed by falling ash, pumice and stones. He described earth shocks so violent it seemed as if the world was not only being shaken, but turned upside down.

I thought it was amazing that the eyewitness account he wrote had come down through the centuries. Only recently did modern scientists realize how accurate Pliny's description was, after they had studied many other volcanoes themselves. I put down my book. From the window I could see Mount Vesuvius, quiet now, looking more like a gentle slumbering hill than a deadly and still-active volcano.

Pliny's description of panicking crowds had been written about the people at Misenum, who had had to shake the ashes off their bodies so they would not be buried alive.

How much worse must it have been for the Herculaneans, who lived closer to the inferno, hemmed in between the mountain and the sea? Vesuvius's blast was so powerful that ash fell as far away as Africa and Syria.

I know many people who get shivers up their spines at the sight of a big lightning storm, or ten-foot waves crashing onto the seashore. But to have the very earth beneath you suddenly gush ash and fire, to have a glowing avalanche of ash and pumice, hotter than an oven, rip over the land at the speed of a galloping horse. . . .

When Vesuvius erupted, ash and gas came spewing out of the summit, forced straight up into the air by the pressure and heat of the blast. Eventually, this cloud cooled, and some of it collapsed, sending ash and hot gas racing down the slopes at

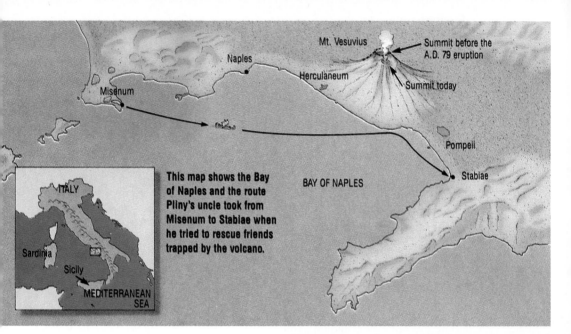

This map shows the Bay of Naples and the route Pliny's uncle took from Misenum to Stabiae when he tried to rescue friends trapped by the volcano.

Far below the earth's surface, gigantic plates of the earth's crust are constantly moving. Where these plates meet, one piece may rub against another, causing an earthquake. But if one plate pushes itself under another, it will melt and become liquid rock or magma. The super-hot liquid rock creates gas and steam, building pressure until it blasts through weak places in the earth's surface. These weak spots are the world's volcanoes.

Above: Vesuvius is located in an area of the world where two plates of the earth's crust meet.

speeds of up to seventy miles per hour, ripping the roofs off houses and overturning ships in the bay. These surges were followed by thick and glowing avalanches of fiery ash, rock and pumice—hot magma that has cooled so quickly that it is still full of volcanic gases, like a hard foamy sponge.

Vesuvius had not actually erupted for hundreds of years before A.D. 79, and the people of the area believed the volcano was extinct. But they could remember an earthquake

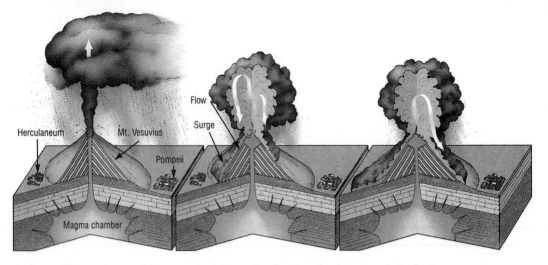

1. At midday on August 24, A.D. 79, Vesuvius erupts, sending a cloud of ash and pumice 12 miles into the air.

2. After midnight, the cloud collapses, sending a surge of ash and hot gas down the mountain, killing the Herculaneans. A flow of hot ash, rock and pumice eventually buries the town.

3. Early the next morning another surge kills the people of Pompeii. It, too, is followed by a flow of hot debris from the volcano.

seventeen years earlier that had caused much damage to the town. And in the days before the volcano erupted, occasional rumblings and ground tremors were felt, creating the odd crack in a wall, or causing a statue to tumble off its stand. And other strange things happened: wells and springs mysteriously dried up, flocks of birds flew away, and animals were exceptionally restless.

We know now that the dry wells were caused by the increasing heat and pressure that were building deep in the earth, and that animals are always more sensitive than humans to changes in the earth and the atmosphere. But, I wondered, were the people in Herculaneum aware that something was about to happen? Before the mountain actually erupted, did it occur to anyone that it might be a good idea to leave town? How many waited until the streets were so crowded that escape was almost impossible? Were they spooked by the tremors, their suddenly dry wells, or the nervous actions of their animals? Did they think the gods were showing their anger?

We will probably never know exactly what the volcano's victims were thinking in those days before the eruption. We do know that the glowing avalanches that buried Herculaneum and the nearby city of Pompeii created two time capsules of ancient Roman life that have not changed in almost two thousand years.

Sealed by volcanic ash and rock, the buried buildings have been protected from the wind and rain that would have worn down the columns and statues over the centuries. Wooden doors, shutters, stairs, cupboards and tables have not been exposed to the air to rot away, or been destroyed by fire. And unlike other ancient towns, the roads and buildings have not been repaired, or torn down and replaced by something more modern.

Instead, Herculaneum and Pompeii look the way they did so many years ago. The roofs of the houses may be gone, the mosaic floors cracked and the wall paintings faded. But we can still walk down the streets over the same stones that the ancient Romans walked on. We can see a 2,000-year-old loaf of bread, now turned to stone, or eggs still in their shells waiting to be served for lunch.

Although both Herculaneum and Pompeii were buried by the volcano, their fates were quite different. Pompeii, a town of twenty thousand people, lay five miles away from the volcano, but the wind was blowing in its direction when the eruption occurred. Throughout the afternoon and evening of August 24th, ash and pumice rained down on Pompeii. This frightened many people, and some of them fled immediately. But it was not until early the next morning that the first flow of hot gas and ash overwhelmed the town, killing the two thousand people who had failed to escape.

The fallen bodies of the Pompeiians were buried under twelve feet of ash and pumice. When the dead bodies rotted away they left hollow places in the hardened volcanic rock. Archaeologists discovered these cavities in the 1860s and decided to pour in plaster to create lifelike models of the volcano's victims as they lay or crouched in the positions in which they died. Some appear to be gasping or choking in their final moments as they were suffocated by ash so hot that it singed their hair and burned the insides of their mouths. But

Archaeologists made lifelike models at Pompeii by pouring plaster into the hollow shells of hardened volcanic rock that sealed Vesuvius's victims.

the plaster also covered up what remained of the skeletons, preventing them from being studied by modern scientists.

Herculaneum, which was less than three miles from Vesuvius, was upwind of the volcano. Most of the falling ash blew in the opposite direction, leaving less than an inch lying over the town by the end of the day. Instead, at about 1:15 early the next morning, a violent surge of ash and hot gas poured over the town. By the time the waves of hot mud followed, everyone was dead. In a few hours, Herculaneum was completely buried under sixty-five feet of hot volcanic matter, which, when it cooled, covered the town like a cement shield.

And so the town lay tightly sealed, for about 1,500 years.

Then in 1709, a well-digger accidentally struck fine polished marble beneath the ground. An Austrian prince who was building a villa in the area realized that the marble was likely just the beginning of a major buried treasure, and he started to dig into the site.

Luckily for the prince, and unhappily for modern archaeologists and historians, the well-digger had found Herculaneum's ancient theater, one of the most luxurious and treasure-filled buildings in the town. The prince wanted art and fine building materials for his villa, so he hired diggers who bored tunnels through the theater, not knowing what it was, and not caring in the least about the damage they were doing to the structure itself.

The prince plundered the building of its bronze and stone statues and vases. Marble was ripped off the walls and pillars, and the treasures were carted off to the prince's own house or those of his rich friends. Before long these valuable artifacts were scattered in museums and private collections all over Europe.

The prince's raiders, burrowing through the site like greedy moles sniffing out treasure, did more damage to Herculaneum than the volcano itself.

More raiding expeditions followed, and it was only in 1860 that serious archaeological work began. But even with many of the most precious objects gone, the excavated town itself told historians a great deal about the ancient Romans and how they lived. Because the ruin had been snugly covered by a wet and heavy layer of earth, Herculaneum was even better preserved than Pompeii (which had suffered more damage under its airy blanket of ash and pumice).

Then just a few years ago came the most amazing discovery of all, when ditch-diggers accidentally found the group of skeletons on the ancient beachfront.

By the time these beach skeletons were found, scientists had discovered that we could learn a great deal about people by examining their bones. We could do much more than make plaster casts. Now we can analyze the bones themselves and reconstruct the skulls to see what the people looked like.

This is where I came in. In the morning, I would help to dig up these bones and begin to study them. For the first time, we would know more about the Romans than what books and paintings and sculptures had shown us. We would be able to see the people themselves.

I would be one of the first modern people to look an ancient Roman in the face.

It was quiet on Herculaneum's ancient beach. Above my head, drying sheets and underwear fluttered from the apartment balconies that now overlook the ruins.

Today this beach is just a narrow dirt corridor that lies several feet below sea level. But thousands of years ago, the waves of the Mediterranean would have lapped where I now stood, and my ears would have been filled with the gentle sound of the surf, rather than the dull roar of midday traffic in modern-day Ercolano, a crowded suburb of Naples.

To one side of me stood the arched entryways of the boat chambers, most of them still plugged by volcanic rock, their secrets locked inside. Only one chamber had been opened so far, and its contents were now hidden behind a padlocked plywood door.

The beachfront, the ruins of Herculaneum and Vesuvius as they look today.
O. Louis Mazzatenta/© The National Geographic Society

I eyed the wooden door longingly, wishing for a sudden gift of X-ray vision. Dr. Maggi, the director of the excavation and keeper of the key, had been called away to a meeting with some government officials, and would not be back until sometime in the afternoon.

"*Dottoressa!*"

Ciro Formuola, the foreman of the work crew that was going to help me dig out the skeletons, was calling me from farther down the old beach. He was waving me toward a roped-off area surrounding three ordinary-looking piles of dirt.

I have examined thousands of skeletons in my life, but seeing each one for the first time still fills me with a kind of awe. As I walked over to the mound that Ciro was pointing at, I knew I was about to meet my first Herculanean.

It didn't look like much at first—just a heap of dirt with bits of bone poking out. I knelt down and gently scraped earth off the skeleton, exposing it to the light for the first time in two thousand years. Although the skeleton was badly broken, I had a hunch that it might be female, but I was puzzled by the position of her bones. Her thigh was poking out grotesquely beside a section of skull. It almost looked as if the bones had been carelessly tossed there, they were so broken and tangled.

Then I realized that something dreadful had happened to this woman, and that she had met with a violent death of some kind. Her skull was shattered, her pelvis crushed, and her leg had been thrust up to her neck. Roof tiles were trapped beneath her.

I looked up. Above me was the open terrace where Herculaneans had held sacred ceremonies. Above that was the wall

I closely examine each bone of a skeleton
as I lift it from the wet volcanic earth.

of the town itself, most of the surrounding balustrade now missing.

Had this woman fallen from the wall above? Had some huge force propelled her from the town, perhaps a piece of flying debris, or the blast from the volcano itself, so that she smashed face down onto the ground? What had she been doing on the wall in the first place? Calling down to the people on the beach for help?

I picked up one of the bones and felt its cool smoothness in my hands. Because this was the first Herculanean I got to know, this skeleton was extra special to me. I named her Portia.

By measuring the bones, I could tell that Portia was about 5 feet 1 inch tall. She was about forty-eight when she died—an old woman by Roman standards—and had buck teeth.

Later, after a chemical analysis, we learned that Portia also had very high levels of lead in her bones. Lead is a poison, but in Roman times it was a common substance. It was used in makeup, medicines, paint pigment, pottery glazes, and to line drinking cups and plates. Cheap wine was sweetened with a syrup that had been boiled down in lead pots, so heavy drinkers may have had even more exposure to lead.

On either side of Portia was a skeleton. One was another female. She lay on her side, almost looking as if she had died in her sleep. As I brushed dirt from her left hand, something shiny caught my eye as it glinted in the sunlight. It was a gold ring.

When we uncovered the rest of the hand, we found a second ring. And in a clump on her hip we found two intricate snakes' head bracelets made of pure gold, a pair of earrings that may have held pearls, and some coins (the cloth purse that had probably once held these valuables had long since rotted away).

We ended up calling her the Ring Lady. She was about forty-five when she died. She was not terribly good-looking; her jaw was large and protruding. There were no cavities in her teeth, but she did have gum disease, which left tiny pits in the bone along her gum line. If she had lived today, her dentist probably would have advised her to floss more often!

In fact, most of the Herculaneans I examined had very good teeth, with only about three cavities each. Today, many of us have about sixteen cavities each, in spite of all our fluoride treatments, regular dental checkups and constant nagging to floss and brush! But the Romans had no sugar in their diet. They used honey, but not much, because it was expensive. Instead, the Herculaneans ate a well-balanced diet, including much seafood, which is rich in fluoride. Not only that, but they had strong jaws from chewing and tearing food

Right: We called this skeleton the Ring Lady because of the two gold rings she wears on her left hand. We also found two bracelets, a pair of earrings and some coins by her side.

O. Louis Mazzatenta/© The National Geographic Society

without using knives and forks. And they did clean their teeth, scrubbing them with the stringy end of a stick rather than using a brush and toothpaste.

On the other side of Portia we dug up the skeleton we called the Soldier. He was found lying down, his hands outstretched, his sword still in his belt. We found carpenter's tools with him, which had perhaps been slung over his back. (Roman soldiers often worked on building projects when they were between wars.) He also had a money belt containing three gold coins. He was quite tall for a Roman, about 5 feet 8 inches.

When I examined the man's skull, I could see that he was missing six teeth, including three at the front, and that he'd had a huge nose. And when I examined the bone of his left thigh, I could see a lump where a wound had penetrated the bone and caused a blood clot that eventually had hardened.

We found these coins in the soldier's money belt. One of them has the head of the Emperor Nero on it.

An archaeologist carefully brushes dirt away from the soldier's skeleton. The soldier's sword still lies by his side.

Near the knee, where the muscle would have been attached, the bone was enlarged slightly. This indicated that he would have had well-developed thighs, possibly due to gripping the sides of a horse with the knees while riding (Romans didn't use saddles).

Had the soldier lost those front teeth in a fight, I wondered. Had he been wounded in the leg during the same fight or another one? His life must have been fairly rough and tumble.

While members of the excavation team poured buckets of water on the three skeletons to loosen the debris, I continued to scrape off the dirt and volcanic matter with a trowel. Later, in the laboratory, each bone and tooth would be washed with a soft brush. Then they would be left to dry before being dipped in an acrylic solution to preserve them. Finally, each bone would be measured, then measured again to prevent errors, and the figures would be carefully recorded.

By late afternoon my back and knees were stiff from crouching, and the back of my neck was tight with the beginning of a sunburn.

I stood up and stretched. There was still much to do before the three skeletons would be free of their volcanic straitjackets. I started to think about heading back to the hotel for a shower and bite to eat. But a flurry of activity down the beach caught my eye, and suddenly I no longer felt tired.

To my right, Dr. Maggi stood outside the locked wooden door I had seen earlier. He was unbolting the padlock. When he saw me, he waved. I put down my trowel, wiped my hands on my jeans and hurried over. Inside, I knew, was the only group of Roman skeletons that had ever been found—the twelve people who had huddled in the shelter and died together when the volcanic avalanches poured down the mountainside into the sea.

I could hear an odd echo from inside the chamber as Dr. Maggi clicked the padlock open. Behind me, a number of the crew members had gathered. We were all very quiet.

The plywood door seemed flimsy as Dr. Maggi pulled it open. From inside the chamber came the dank smell of damp earth.

A shiver crept up my neck. We were opening a 2,000-year-old grave. What would we find?

As I entered the cave-like boat chamber, I could barely see, even though the sun flooded through the door. Someone handed me a flashlight, but its light cast greenish shadows, making it feel even more spooky.

The light played over the back of the shelter, no bigger than a single garage and still crusted over with volcanic rock. I saw an oddly shaped, lumpy mound halfway back. I took several steps into the chamber and pointed the light at the mound.

The narrow beam found a skull, the pale face a grimace of death. As my eyes grew accustomed to the dim light, I soon realized there were bones and skulls everywhere. They were all tangled together—clinging to each other for comfort in their final moments—and it was hard to distinguish one from another. But I knew that twelve skeletons had been found in all—three men, four women, and five children. One child had an iron house key near him. Did he think he would be going back home?

I took another step into the cave. At my feet was a skeleton that was almost entirely uncovered. From the pelvis I could see it was a female, a girl, lying face down. Beneath her, we could just see the top of another small skull.

It was a baby.

I knelt down and gently touched the tiny skull. My throat felt tight as I thought about this girl, this baby, and what it must have been like for them in this dark cave in the moments before they died.

"*Una madre col suo bambino,*" whispered Ciro behind me.

"I don't think they're a mother and baby," I said. I could see from the pelvis that the girl was not old enough to have had children. I pointed to my own stomach and outlined a beach-ball tummy with my arms while I shook my head. "This girl has never given birth."

"*Allora, é la sorella?*"

I frowned, pulled my Italian-English dictionary out of the back pocket of my jeans and flipped through it. I realized Ciro thought these two skeletons belonged to a baby and its older sister.

"We'll see," I murmured. I knew it was important not to jump to conclusions. You have to question everything about bones, especially ones that have been lying around for two thousand years. I've known cases where people thought bone damage was caused by joint disease, when it was in fact caused by rats gnawing at the dead body.

I struggled to free a bronze cupid pin and two little bells from the baby's bones. Whoever the child was, it had been rich enough to wear expensive ornaments. But I knew it

One of our most moving finds was the skeleton of a young slave girl
cradling the tiny skull of a baby. With these two skeletons, the tragedy of
that terrible day in A.D. 79 became very real to us.

O. Louis Mazzatenta/© The National Geographic Society

would take many more hours of careful study before we knew
the real story behind these two skeletons.

Later, in the laboratory, I gained enough information to put
together a more likely background for the skeleton of the
young girl.

Unlike the baby, she had not come from a wealthy family.
She had been about fourteen, and from the shape of her skull
I knew she had probably been pretty. When I examined her
teeth I could tell that she had been starved or quite ill for a
time when she was a baby. She had also had two teeth
removed about one or two weeks before she died, probably

giving her a fair bit of pain. And her life had been very hard. She had done a lot of running up and down stairs or hills, as well as having to lift objects too heavy for her delicate frame.

This girl could not have been the child of a wealthy family, like the baby. She had probably been a slave who died trying to protect the baby of the family she worked for.

And there were many others. Near the slave girl lay the skeleton of a seven-year-old girl whose bones also showed that she had done work far too heavy for a child so young.

We found a sixteen-year-old fisherman, his upper body well developed from rowing boats, his teeth worn from holding cord while he repaired his fishing nets.

Particularly heartbreaking were the two pregnant women I examined, for we were also able to recover their tiny unborn babies, their bones as fragile as eggshells. One woman had been only about sixteen years old.

Though it is fascinating to reconstruct the life of a single person by examining his or her bones, for anthropologists and historians the most useful information comes from examining all of the skeletons of one population. This is one reason why Herculaneum is so important.

During the next few months we opened two more boat chambers. In one we discovered forty tangled human skeletons and one of a horse; in another we found twenty-six skeletons creepily lined up like a row of dominoes, as if heading in single file for the back of the chamber.

The skeletons represented a cross-section of the population of a whole town—old people, children and babies, slaves, rich and poor, men and women, the sick and the healthy. By examining all these skeletons, we can get some ideas about how the townspeople lived and what they were like physically.

We found out, for example, that the average Herculanean man was 5 feet 5 inches tall, the average woman about 5 feet 1 inch. In general, they were well nourished. And we have examined enough people to know that although the rich people had easy lives, the slaves often worked so hard that they were in pain much of the time.

Studying these skeletons closely can also help medical researchers and doctors. In ancient times, many diseases could not be cured by surgery or drugs. Instead, people kept getting sicker, until they eventually died. By examining the bones of these people, we can learn a great deal about how certain diseases progress.

By the end of my stay in Herculaneum, I had examined 139 skeletons. Their bones were sorted into yellow plastic

Excavators have nearly cleared one of these boat chambers, but the one next to it is still blocked by hard volcanic rock.

O. Louis Mazzatenta/© The National Geographic Society

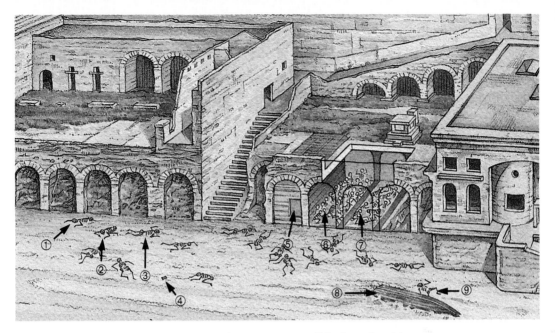

The illustration shows how the ancient seawall looks today. Altogether, we excavated over one hundred skeletons from the beach and boat chambers. 1. The Ring Lady   2. Portia   3. The Soldier   4. Coin box   5. Chamber with 26 skeletons inside   6. Chamber with 40 skeletons inside, including one of a horse   7. Chamber with 12 skeletons inside   8. The boat 9. A slave, perhaps a fisherman

vegetable crates that lined the shelves in my laboratory. And each box of bones has a different story to tell.

Even though I can't tell the good guys from the bad, and I can't tell you whether they were happy or not, I know a great deal about these people. I can see each person plainly. I even imagine them dressed as they might have been, lounging on their terraces or in the baths if they were wealthy, toiling in a mine or in a galley if they were the most unfortunate slaves.

Most of all, I feel that these people have become my friends, and that I have been very lucky to have had a part in bringing their stories to the rest of the world.

HIS MAJESTY, QUEEN HATSHEPSUT

Dorothy Sharp Carter
illustrated by Michele Chessare

In Egypt in about the year 1503 B.C.,
Queen Hatshepsut, daughter of King Thutmose I, wife of King
Thutmose II, ascends the throne at her husband's death. But it
is a throne she shares as Queen Regent with her nine-year-old
stepson, Prince Thutmose III. Sharing the throne with the
prince displeases Queen Hatshepsut. Two years into her reign,
she has a dream in which the King of Gods, Amon-Re, tells
Hatshepsut's mother that Hatshepsut "shall exercise the
excellent kingship of this whole land."

Queen Hatshepsut uses the dream as an excuse
to hold a coronation and have herself declared King of Upper
and Lower Egypt, a bold and audacious act. How can this be?
A woman who is king? Some of the men in her court are angry
at her brazen deed, especially the priests who want Prince
Thutmose to become king as soon as he comes of age.
But King Hatshepsut triumphs and rules Egypt until her death
twenty-two years later.

You are about to meet King Hatshepsut and discover
what her life was like in a civilization that no longer exists.

🪓 *218* 🪓

YEAR 3 OF THE REIGN OF
HIS MAJESTY MAKARE HATSHEPSUT

"Day 14, month 3 of Sowing . . . " While only three months have passed since my coronation, I date my reign as beginning from the death of my husband. It gives a more settled appearance. And in truth I did begin my rule then, for what use was the presence of a nine-year-old boy?

I, Makare Hatshepsut, am Pharaoh of the whole of Egypt, with no fetters, no restraints to hinder me. I know now how a caged bird feels when at long last the door flaps open and it can escape into the limitless blue of heaven.

It is not that I desire power for its own sake. I am not so vainglorious. But to have the authority to do what I know must be done for my country's good—that is ecstasy. Also— to be completely truthful—I desire to demonstrate to Egypt, to the entire world, that a woman can rule every bit as wisely as a man.

Each morning when Henut wakes me, I lie for a moment not thinking at all, only savoring this enormous bubble of happiness. Arching my neck over the cushioned headrest of my bed, I watch a sliver of sunlight enter the high window and light up the curly frieze border of the ceiling. The chariot of Amon begins its journey across the clear sky just as I am about to begin *my* day.

For another moment I ponder my goals as ruler. I will make Egypt stronger than she has ever been—so strong internally that no country will ever dare challenge her.

I will repair all the temples in the land, in particular those which the vagabond foreign rulers of Egypt, the Hyksos, neglected for so long. In addition, I will construct others to be the most beautiful in the world.

And—an idea lodged in a far corner of my mind—I may in time launch a sailing expedition to Punt, that faraway place we know as God's Land, the source of our indispensable frankincense and myrrh. This can in name be a trading expedition, but in fact a purpose just as important will be to explore, to observe the wonders of the Great Green [the Red Sea], of the manners and customs of the Puntites, of the nature of their land. I may command that expedition myself. For I am immensely inquisitive about foreign peoples, how they live and dress and think. Curiosity may be a queenly rather than kingly trait, but in any case, I intend to indulge it.

"It is the hour, Highness."

Henut stands beside my bed, a fresh linen robe in her hands. I slip into the robe, into my sandals. Henut runs a comb through my hair, adjusts a heavy, elaborate wig. I am ready for the first ritual of the morning.

Outside the door wait two high priestesses of Amon, one wearing the mask of Horus, the other the ibis head of Thoth. They bow. We walk in silence down the hall to the House of the Morning, my main chapel.

Inside, the golden ewers of water stand ready on a marble-topped table. Removing my robe, I lave my body, speaking aloud a prayer.

"Great Father God Amon-Re, as thou bathest in the ocean each morning to begin thy journey across the heavens, so bathes thy daughter. Thus we restore our divine vitality for the day's tasks. Guide me, O my father, to live in *maat* for today and always."

The priestesses anointing me, helping to robe me, are a symbol of triumph. They are the result of my first victory as ruler over Amon's priesthood.

The day I ascended the throne, a chief priest informed me, "Each morning two priestesses will accompany Her Majesty to the House of the Morning. As Her Majesty may know, a king is attended by priests wearing the masks of Horus and Thoth. This would of course be unsuitable in the case of Her Majesty." His voice held an edge of superiority.

"Perhaps my proclamation has not reached your ears, Lord," I replied icily. "My Majesty, being king, is referred to by the whole world as *His* Majesty. Furthermore, the priestesses will naturally don the masks of Horus and Thoth."

Shock and indignation so overcame him that he stammered. "S-such a custom is unheard of in the en-entire h-history of the Two Lands!" He glared at me, suddenly realized who—or what—I was, and gulped.

"I beg Her . . . His Majesty's pardon, but for women . . . priestesses to wear the sacred masks defies the holy tradition of Amon's ritual."

"Then we will change tradition. See that the female Thoth and Horus await My Majesty tomorrow." I dismissed him brusquely. He stumbled away, his face pale even for a priest.

They resent me, the priests, and will yet cause me trouble—I sense it. Despite all I do for Amon. However, for the time all goes well. With use customs come quickly to be accepted, and after three months the priestesses and their masks have become routine.

After my ablutions we proceed to another chapel, already occupied by priests and court officials. Here more prayers are said, and a high priest intones, "May a curse be laid, O Amon, on anyone who offends thee, with or without intention."

Later the same priest feels called on to reassure me. "The curse is aimed at His Majesty's ministers, certainly not at His Majesty himself." But swiftly adds, "His Majesty takes note, I am sure, of all prayers as a guide to royal conduct."

His tone reminds me of Tutami in the classroom: condescending patronage. At times—many times—the priesthood takes on the all-powerful airs of Amon. It could do with a lesson in humility.

Sacrifice and the reading of the entrails follow: A priest spells out the omens. The day is auspicious for the composing of letters, for the holding of audience, for the visiting of friends. Inauspicious for journeys, either by boat or palanquin or foot. (That I could have forecast myself. There is enough work to keep me occupied at home for some time.)

At last I am escorted back to my quarters. After perfuming my mouth with wine and fruit, I submit to being readied. It is a quiet time to think and plan.

Were I a man, I could confer with my officials while being groomed. However, most of my council would die of embarrassment if called on to witness the plucking of my brows, the massage with unguents, the application of kohl and henna. As a dozen corpses would be of no help to me, I think alone.

One problem is that of Prince Thutmose. How he views my dream of divine birth I do not know. Nor do I care. Deep in my mind this lack of interest concerning Thutmose bothers me. Thorough and careful always in my planning, I do not forget the obstacles, however small, which like sharp stones protrude through the path of my life.

The Prince is such an obstacle. He is more than a stone. Rather, he is a vein of rock that appears treacherously now here, now there, for me to stumble over. One day he may loom before me, a high jagged barrier.

Well. The rock lies there, I am aware of it, and there is nothing to do about it. For the time being.

Yesterday Hapusoneb made a suggestion: Why did I not place the Prince under his care as apprentice priest? It is an honor due a prince to serve the Great God of No-Amon. There he would be under the eye of the entire priesthood.

Under *your* eye, O Hapusoneb, perhaps. The entire priesthood may not be so trustworthy. At all events, the idea has merit and I shall consider it.

While my hair is being dressed, I glance over accounts of palace expenditures. To think I once complained (to be truthful not once but many times) of having to learn to read. How thoughtless children are. True it is they do not know what is good for them.

The palace expenses are revealing. So much waste. No doubt kings seldom pay heed to such petty details, but this is a field I can understand and correct. Not only disbursements of the Great House but those made throughout the government can and shall be curtailed. Some officials act as though the lotuses of the Nile were of gold and have only to be plucked. They shall learn.

As an example, I have cut my immediate toilet staff to twenty. My husband had twice that number, including four barbers to shave him when he surely had beard enough for one alone.

I have limited my attendants to one mat spreader, two manicurists and two pedicurists (all four work at once to save time), three hairdressers, two masseuses, four perfumers (well, one to daub on scent and three others to distill the oils and mix the fragrances), one to prepare my bath, two to dress me, two to apply cosmetics, one to adjust my jewelry (my mother used three such, but to her all jewels were lucky or unlucky depending on the day, and this had to be determined by divination). I do not count laundresses, bleachers, pressers, seamstresses.

Today, with one public appearance, and that an informal one, I will dress as a woman. That means a gown instead of a kilt, a light wig, and crown. What an advantage I have over other pharaohs. I can choose my sex as it pleases me.

A whisper. "Majesty?"

The Keeper of Royal Jewelry stands before me, a tray of gold collars in her hands. They are too heavy, appropriate for formal functions. I shake my head and wave her away to fetch other, lighter necklets.

She returns with a necklace of thin gold wires woven about delicate flowers of pearls and amethysts. And with it my favorite earrings, those the Great God Pharaoh, my father, presented me when I was nine. They are butterflies, their wings of lapis lazuli and garnet, fastened to gold loops. I nod. Why cannot one's officials be as eager and amenable as servants?

A discreet cough disturbs my musing. "Your Majesty."

Only Henut dares interrupt my thoughts. I glance up.

My twenty attendants stand in stiff rows like soldiers, their gaze on the floor. Henut stands before them, her eyes plucking their stance, their hands, their expression, as she would pluck feathers from a goose. If any is found wanting, that one will know shortly.

It appears I am readied for the day.

First is scheduled a conference with Chief Treasurer Nehesi. Nehesi is the newest of my councillors, unearthed by Hapusoneb, my faithful minister of a myriad connections.

The Treasurer is a small man, as shriveled as a dried fig. Son of a Nubian brewer, he completely lacks the elegance and assurance of the average courtier. Far more important, he knows and understands value.

For years he was a middleman at the market, dealing in that unit of commerce called the *shat*. Father once explained to me the meaning of the word.

"As an example, my daughter, let us take the seller of a cow. In exchange for it, he is offered so many bushels of corn or lengths of linen or jars of wine. But, being fond of his cow, he decides the animal is worth more than what is offered. The difference then must be calculated in so many *shat*, and an item of that worth agreed on."

"I should not at all mind doing such work," I told him. "To aid seller and purchaser to find articles of equal value—it is a kind of game."

Father chuckled (I was the cause of many of his smiles and laughs). "A kind of game, yes. Didst thou know, Hatshepsut, that some countries base their unit of value on metal, copper or silver or gold?"

I put my nose in the air. "That would be a clumsy system, metal being so heavy and cumbersome."

Father nodded. "A practice to be expected of foreign lands."

Well, what else? In its ideas and practices my Egypt is years in advance of other nations.

Father would have approved of Nehesi: his careful honesty, his tenacity, his precision, his refusal to be intimidated . . . except by *me*. My Treasurer has yet to figure me out and tends to handle me as gingerly as he would an ostrich egg.

Our conference goes well—better for me than for him. After the usual review of revenue and disbursement, he hesitantly broaches a new subject.

"Your Majesty, the Chief Steward brings to my attention"— he pauses, coughs nervously—"a trivial matter. Of very minor

importance." He stops again, struggles to heave up the words he wants. He takes a deep breath, and lo, the words come gushing forth. "Your Majesty, there are complaints from the royal household regarding the inadequate ration of bread." He bows his head. (For me to strike it off?)

I allow my arched brows to arch higher. "How is this possible? Do we not provide fourteen hundred loaves a day?"

"Indeed, your Majesty. Oh, indeed. His Majesty may be unaware that Great God-King Thutmose made provision for *two thousand* loaves daily."

"Treasurer, my staff is much reduced from that era. There is now no harem, and fewer personal attendants."

"True, true. But . . . to maintain His Majesty's residence in the appropriate style for a monarch of His Majesty's glorious status, an adequate household staff is absolutely necessary. The staff has grown, of necessity with His Majesty's tremendous responsibilities, to a somewhat greater size than that of the Great God-King Thutmose II. . . ."

Here he marks my frown at mention of my husband's name and leaps to a happier note. "His Majesty will be most gratified to learn that—this from a memorandum of the Chief Steward—the palace has decreased the amount of beer consumed from 200 to 150 jugs a day. Except, of course, when the amount is augmented for holidays."

Which means ten days out of thirty. My subjects live for feast days.

"My Majesty is well pleased about the beer. But back to the bread. My Majesty detests waste and will not provide for gorging."

The Treasurer is unused to women who argue and is thrown off balance. "Your Highness, could we . . . if I may . . . Your Majesty, with the addition of two hundred loaves more, I believe there would be no waste. And no further complaints."

I ponder. An idea sprouts, leafs out, flowers. It is a good idea and has additional merit: It will flick the priesthood's too-haughty nose.

"Lord Nehesi, the state is making major repairs and improvements on Amon's temple. My Majesty has in mind rich gifts, additions to the temple such as statues, obelisks, fine new ceremonial robes for the priests. In return for these, we will request the temple to supply the Great House with two hundred loaves of bread daily."

My Treasurer smiles thinly. Still overawed by a female sovereign, he cannot believe I am serious in demanding bread from Amon's domain. On discovering that I mean what I say, he wonders if the temple will blame *him* for the proposal, which could have uncomfortable effects; the priesthood can be vindictive in subtle ways.

I have faith in Nehesi's astuteness. Blame can be shared by the Chief Steward, by a dozen other officials. At any rate, I have solved that problem with no increase in my budget. My people will not say of me, "Ah! She flings gold dust about as though it were sand."

Actually Egypt's finances are at present in excellent shape. Our hundreds of granaries in temples and towns are well stocked in the event of a light inundation and the resulting failure of crops. The construction of private buildings is brisk, bringing in good revenue from the state monopoly in brick making; the same is true in papermaking. Fortunately for me, taxation on harvests and ships and property need not be increased this year.

A thought occurs: With my head so full of economies, large and small, I could always find occupation as a simple housewife!

Next on my schedule, I show myself for the first time as Pharaoh at the Window of Appearances. My excuse to the Vizier is that the people adore spectacles of any sort, and a view of Pharaoh is regarded as a grand treat. To be quite honest, I do it for pure pleasure. To distribute largesse in my own name, with no one to nod me permission—ah, I relish that.

Always before, I had stood behind my father or my husband and was handed a small bracelet or two to toss. Today Nefrure alone appears with me. She bounces with anticipation.

"Calm thyself," I chide her.

"Oh, my mother, I do not like to be calm!"

She peers over the railing at the courtyard. It being a hot and windless day, the court is packed with sunshade bearers and fan bearers as well as household officials and relatives of the honorees. A guard marshals the recipients into a queue. On three sides the public, wiping their perspiring faces, strain against the ropes. Even the lowliest wears a clean loincloth for the occasion.

There are seven or eight honorees. As each steps before the balcony and salutes me, I deliver a short speech of praise, ending with "Thou art my faithful servant who hast carried out the orders of My Majesty, who is well pleased with thee. I therefore award thee these gifts with the words 'Thou shalt eat the bread of Pharaoh (Life, Health, Strength!) thy lord, in the temple of Amon.'"

From the tray of gold ornaments I choose necklets, rings, inlaid hatchets, goblets, trinkets in the shapes of bees and lions, to fling to those honored. As the gifts are caught, there are shrieks of delight from the family.

Nefrure is in raptures. She helps to shower "the praise of gold" on her friends Hapusoneb (honored for faithful and meritorious service) and Senmut (for outstanding ideas concerning efficiency and economies in government departments). They will need to grow new necks to wear all the chains she flings to them.

"Senmut needs another bracelet!" Nefrure exclaims, eyes bright with excitement. As I have appointed him her tutor, she sees much of him. They have grown very fond of each other.

"He will not be able to wear so much jewelry or carry it either," I protest. "There will be other opportunities."

"Tomorrow?" she asks hopefully.

I laugh. "Not tomorrow, but very soon."

The last award goes to the Keeper of the Interior Apartments for long and industrious service. "Meritorious" and "outstanding" can certainly not be applied to him, nor I fear, can "faithful." The ceremony will reduce the sting when tomorrow I replace him in office. He is a relic of my husband's

rule, disapproves vocally of queen rulers, and treats with no merchant or servant without a fat bribe. His wife is as oily as he, her eyes as shifty as his as she peeps into my face, incredulous that a mere *woman* is capable of filling the throne of the Two Lands. Stupid creature! Ah well, after today I will see little of them. He will be offered the position of Messenger for the Dogs' Food, which he is not likely to accept.

After lunch I escape to my refuge, a chamber furnished with only a long sofa and a small table to hold refreshments. With no other clutter, I can imagine I am on my country estate, the tiles of the floor tinted green as grass, the ceiling molded and painted to resemble a grape arbor, the vines thick with purple fruit.

Here I admit only Henut, to massage my forehead for headache, and my daughter (during those rare moments when she agrees to act like a lady). Today I have invited Senmut— Lord Senmut, as he has been for a month.

Senmut. Ah, Hatshepsut, in spite of thy royal and divine blood and against thy strongest wishes, thou art proved to be all too mortal. To hear the name of Senmut, to glimpse Senmut, to hear Senmut's voice—my breath, my blood cease in their courses, my vision clouds, my ears ring, my head is light.

What does it mean? Surely not that I love him. I have never loved anyone—apart from my dear Egypt—besides my father, and my daughter. I do not allow myself to love anyone. I cannot afford to. Love is weakness. I tell myself that over and over: Love is weakness. Only . . . how do I control my blood, my breath?

I question myself severely. Why do I find this man appealing? He is not handsome, although his face is unique, the features clear cut like his character, mouth thin, eyes both wide and long. The nose is somewhat hooked but not, thanks be to Hathor, as prominent as my own family's nose. The mobility of expression constitutes its charm.

His most significant traits are his boldness of outlook, his self-assurance, his adaptability. As my daughter's tutor he has proved his gentleness, for she can tax one's patience with her teasing.

I say that he is adaptable; already he has adopted the dress, the manners, the carriage, the viewpoint of a nobleman. No. In all frankness he has not done so completely.

With regard to the gods, I have noticed, he is unsophisticated and highly superstitious. And he possesses a peasant's unabashed urge for acquisition. The offices I appoint him to he fulfills without fault. But the titles of those offices he collects and wears as a rustic woman flaunts at one time every string of cheap beads she owns. On all letters, all proclamations, Senmut never fails to include each and every title. Still, modesty is by no means a national characteristic of ours.

Today I confer with Senmut in his new capacity as Controller of Works. We will discuss the reopening of our copper and turquoise mines in the Sinai. (My composure is flawless. No blush, no tremble, no shortness of breath is apparent.)

"The reworking of the mines," I explain, "will require the presence of troops to ensure security from the barbaric sand dwellers. Aside from protection, the project will serve to keep the men occupied. The officers tend to become quickly restless unless they are busy warring and conquering."

Having been at one time a military scribe, Senmut is aware of how the military mind works. He nods.

"The plan is good. The officers will welcome it more than their men."

I look at him inquiringly.

"The common soldiers dislike setting foot on foreign soil. They ask, 'What if we die there? Who will prepare our bodies for burial? Who will recite the ritual over us? Are we to lose eternity because we leave our beloved Egypt?' I fear you must count on some desertions."

An idea comes to mind. These days find me as full of ideas as a palm tree with dates. I make haste to pluck the ideas and put them to work before they rot on the branches. "I will see that a body of priests and two or three embalmers accompany the men. That should allay their fear."

And if I follow Hapusoneb's suggestion of placing the Prince under his supervision as an apprentice priest—which appears most reasonable—then in two or three years' time the boy can himself become part of such an expedition to Sinai. It will provide him training and experience. And it will remove him effectively from the scene of action—for a time.

"That will cheer the men." Senmut's tone approves my decision.

"Have you yourself lived away from Egypt?" I ask.

"At one time. I built a grain warehouse and later the courthouse for the colony that Great Pharaoh Thutmose II" —he bows his head—"established in Cush."

"You engineered those buildings?"

He grimaces slightly. "They were nothing. But seeing them, the general Huy requested me to construct a house in the country for his newly married daughter. *That* I was proud of."

"So you are an architect." Is there no end to this man's talents? "Have you constructed other edifices?"

"A new home for my parents. My tomb and theirs. The deepest joy of life comes from creating a structure—a cottage, a mansion, a palace."

"In which of these did you grow up?"

"The first, Your Majesty. My father is a farmer, and his farm is very small."

"Then you have done doubly well." I contemplate another idea. With deliberation I ask, "Have you ever dreamed of designing a temple? A mortuary temple?"

Senmut draws in a deep breath, holds it for a full minute. His eyes, fixed on my feet, have turned to glass.

The breath pours out in a sigh, and his eyes meet mine. "A dream far beyond hope. Does His Majesty have such a temple in mind?"

Lord Senmut wastes no time in circling a subject. He even takes away *my* breath.

"The place for a temple, yes," I say slowly. "The shape of the temple itself, no." I change my tone to one of indifference. "Should you be interested, you might submit a plan."

He is at once all business. "Indeed, Majesty, I am interested. Would you tell me the site of this temple?"

"Near the tomb of Great Pharaoh Mentuhotep, built some six hundred years ago. As you are aware, it lies close to the valley where my own father is buried."

"It is a magnificent setting. Oh yes. Precisely right for a temple." Already his mind is churning, his eyes bright, his face flushed with the challenge.

To my chagrin I find myself jealous of this challenge. Would his face liven, his eyes glow so fervently if he thought of me as "Hatshepsut" rather than as "His Majesty"? Or—terrible thought—does he use me only to further his ambition? Ah, what a tangle is life! The lowly alone can afford to be direct. I dismiss Lord Senmut with a cool smile.

One further task remains to be done this day. During a short visit to the temple of Amon to view the alterations, I have an interview with my stepson, who has his lessons there. He is not a likable boy. The royal blood in him is so weakened by the common fluid of his mother that he is little better than a peasant. And looks it. Even for eleven years he is thin and knobby. How Egypt would fare under his rule I tremble to think. We will put it off as long as possible. Perhaps forever.

The Third Priest of Amon, Lord Rensonb, is also present. He is a lean, cold, unyielding man with a head like a skull, a fanatic fervor for detail, and a sensitive stomach. According to Hapusoneb, his moods match the state of this organ, which is generally sour.

The story goes that upon learning that I was to ascend the throne, he threw himself on the temple floor before the shrine of Amon and declared that he would die there of starvation rather than see a woman as king. His miserable stomach saved his life; its protest at being denied sustenance was more than he could bear. However, instead of blaming his stomach for his failure, he blamed me.

I nod to Rensonb and address the Prince. "My Majesty has decided to place thee in the Great Temple in order to serve Amon. Would this please thee?"

I sound pompous without meaning to. The boy makes me uncomfortable, he is always so silent and noncommittal.

"I thank thee, yes, gracious Majesty." His voice is shrill, the words are sedate, his glance never lifts from the floor.

"Good. The lord Hapusoneb will oversee thy duties."

He bows, saying nothing.

I turn to the Third Priest.

"Then, Lord, My Majesty leaves the Prince in your hands in the hope he will do honor to the God of Gods."

Never one for humility, the Third Priest must have his say. "His Majesty may rest assured. As the future ruler of the Two Lands, the Prince will be given the best of training."

"For that reason My Majesty places him here." My tone is curt.

"The best of training. And the most intensive. Within three or four years the Prince will be prepared to take his place as king."

I am floored by his presumption. My temper, as uncontrollable as Rensonb's stomach, boils up.

"*When* he becomes king is no concern of yours, Lord Rensonb. As director of the temple school you will superintend his education. From First Prophet Hapusoneb My Majesty will receive reports of the Prince's progress—and of *your* efficiency as educator."

I turn my back on him, nod farewell to Thutmose. For once the boy's face is less impassive than a toad's. The exchange of words has actually upset him; his mouth is wide open as he bows.

It has upset me, also. Were the Third Priest any other man, I would replace him immediately, expel him to some small temple in Cush. But Rensonb's family is as old as my own and was at one time as noble. The manner of ridding myself of him must be subtle. Meanwhile, under Hapusoneb's eye he will hesitate to plant seditious ideas in my stepson's head—I trust.

My conversation with Senmut comes to mind, and a vague scheme grows strong. Very well, little son. Within the year thou wilt journey to the Sinai—well away from Rensonb and from thy mother, Isis—where thy stamina and character will be tested. The desert is an oven and abounds in snakes and poisonous insects, wild and wily tribesmen who resent intrusion. If thou weatherest all these, young Prince, thou mayest acquire worthy blood on thy own. In time—years and years from now—thou mayest even succeed me. *If* no one more suitable appears.

Back at the palace, a scroll is handed me, and my dejection vanishes. It is a sketch, very rough, of Senmut's design for my temple. He has taken the plan of Mentuhotep's shrine but enlarged and improved on it. The longer I study it, the more I feel it can be worked into a superb model. Mine will be the most beautiful temple, the most magnificent building in all the Two Lands! And justly so, for I wish to be remembered always as a queen who became a king . . . a king greatest of the great.

The location is a kind of amphitheater, and the backdrop of my temple consists of high, rugged, towering cliffs. Instead of a tall, imposing structure that would be lost against the steep cliffs, Senmut has drawn a low but extremely wide building. There are three ascending terraces, like gigantic steps, connected by ramps. Each terrace consists of a huge courtyard leading into a colonnaded hall, the roof of each hall forming

the courtyard of the hall above. The complex will be immense; we Egyptians build big, as we think big.

The glory of the plan is in its contrast to the background and in its simplicity. Even the terraces resemble my vision of the myrrh terraces of Punt, the original garden of the gods.

I am too excited by the plan to think. Originally I had thought to require plans from a half dozen of No-Amon's finest architects. Now there is no need. No one in the entire world or in the next thousand years could conceive a design so exactly right. Had I been an artist, I should myself have designed a temple just so. Of course it is still a sketch only, a bare outline—but oh, it has promise.

Tomorrow I will announce my acceptance of the plan to the Great Ones, my council, and give orders to begin work as soon as possible. The embellishment of halls and courtyards can be worked out later. The matter itself is settled.

This means, too, that I will see much of Lord Senmut. Hat-shepsut, reel in thy heart before it dies of throbbing! So be it. As I rise, so Senmut shall rise.

He is vital, dynamic . . . almost an extension of myself. I even feel he understands me—which certainly no one else living does. With all my wariness and distrust, I do not mind this. Even a pharaoh needs someone to understand him. But only *one* someone, no more. And this someone I will make to love me. Truly love me.

"Hathor, dear goddess of love, I will have Senmut build thee an altar!" I whisper. "Thanks upon thanks I send thee. Thou hast blessed me with someone to love. . . . I will have the most splendid temple in Egypt. . . . The Prince's future is decided. . . . Above all, I am King of the Two Lands! No, Hathor, thou deservest more than an altar. I will build thee a chapel within my very own temple!"

Even for a pharaoh, joy does not endure. But this day I will forever remember as joyful.

PRINCIPAL CHARACTERS AND GODS

Amon—*god of the sun, chief god of No-Amon*
Hapusoneb—*Hatshepsut's Vizier, First Prophet of Amon, and member of her Council of Goverment*
Hathor—*goddess of love and beauty*
Henut—*Hatshepsut's childhood nurse and later her maid*
Horus—*god of the sun*
Isis—*mother of Thutmose III*
Nefrure—*daughter of Hatshepsut and Thutmose II*
Nehesi—*Chief Treasurer and leader of the expedition to Punt*
Rensonb—*Third Priest of Amon and an ally of Thutmose III*
Senmut—*Hatshepsut's favorite courtier and chief adviser*
Thoth—*god of learning and magic*
Thutmose I—*Pharaoh and father of Hatshepsut*
Thutmose II—*Pharaoh and husband of Hatshepsut*
Thutmose III—*son of Thutmose II and Isis; stepson of Hatshepsut*
Tutami—*tutor of Hatshepsut and her brothers*

MEET DOROTHY SHARP CARTER, AUTHOR

Dorothy Sharp Carter read of Queen Hatshepsut's life in Will Durant's Story of Civilization *and became fascinated by a queen who became pharaoh, at a time when queens were not allowed to rule. Carter was also fascinated with the history and customs of ancient Egypt. She combined knowledge of Egypt's history and customs with the few known facts about the queen's life. Then, with her writer's imagination, she created the story of* His Majesty, Queen Hatshepsut.

MEET MICHELE CHESSARE, ILLUSTRATOR

Michele Chessare did not know much about Egyptian art or culture before undertaking the illustrations for His Majesty, Queen Hatshepsut. *To research her topic, she explored the Egyptian wing of the Metropolitan Museum of Art in New York and studied books on Egypt from libraries. "That's what's so nice about this job [illustrating]. Sometimes you get to research things that you otherwise wouldn't have known about," she says.*

Since there are no photographs from the time of Queen Hatshepsut, Chessare studied Egyptian drawings and statues to get a feel for how people of that time dressed and looked. Then she made her figures and scenes as realistic as possible.

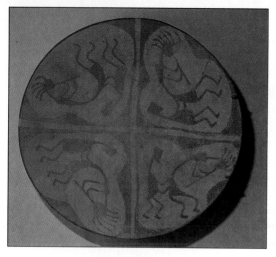

Dish decorated with flute player. 10th century.
Hohokam culture.

Clay. Arizona State Museum. Photo: Werner Forman
Archive/Art Resource

Excavated pottery from the site
of the palace at Knossos, Crete, Greece.
c. 2000–1400 B.C.

Photo: Michos Tzovaras/Art Resource

Painting of a mural from the Maya
city of Uaxactún. 1959. Antonio Tevedaf.

Museo Nacional de Arqueología y Etnología, Guatemala City.
Photo: © Mireille Vautier/Woodfin Camp & Associates

FINE ART
ANCIENT
CIVILIZATIONS

Seated figure of
Queen Hatshepsut. 18th Dynasty,
c. 1490–1470 B.C. Egyptian.

Pink granite. Egyptian Collection, Oudheden
Museum, Rijksmuseum, Leiden.
Photo: © Erich Lessing/Art Resource

Medallion showing bust of young
man reading a scroll. 1st century A.D.
Herculaneum, Italy.

Fresco. National Archaeological Museum, Naples. Photo:
© Erich Lessing/Art Resource

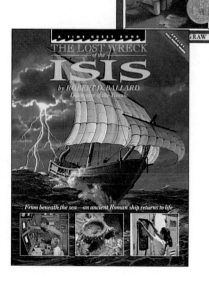

BIBLIOGRAPHY

Boy of the Painted Cave by Justin Denzel. Tao, a boy who lives in prehistoric times, is forced out of his clan into the wilderness and must learn to survive on his own.

The Castle Story by Sheila Sancha. This intriguing volume describes ninety-three castles in Great Britain and Ireland and tells the story of the people who once inhabited them.

The Golden Goblet by Eloise Jarvis McGraw. In this tale, set in ancient Egypt, Ranofer longs to become a goldsmith, but his abusive stepbrother has other ideas. Learn how the golden goblet changes Ranofer's life.

The Lost Wreck of the Isis by Robert D. Ballard. Ballard and his team of underwater archaeologists explore the cerulean waters of the Mediterranean at the site where a Roman ship sank in the fourth century A.D.

Maroo of the Winter Caves by Ann Turnbull. Maroo and her brother, Otak, brave freezing temperatures and icy winds to find shelter for their family during a very harsh winter in the Late Ice Age.

New Treasures of the Past by Brian Fagan. Within the pages of this fascinating book, which includes beautiful photographs, you'll learn about some of archaeology's most recent findings.

Pompeii: Exploring a Roman Ghost Town by Ron and Nancy Goor. This book re-creates the ancient city and society of Pompeii by analyzing artifacts, existing buildings, ruins, and graffiti.

Turtle People by Brenda Z. Guiberson. Eleven-year-old Richie visits a remote island near his Washington State home and discovers a mysterious artifact. Can he solve the riddle of the object's past?

TAKING A STAND

THE PRETTY PENNIES PICKET

from PHILIP HALL LIKES ME.
I RECKON MAYBE. by Bette Greene
illustrated by Colin Bootman

I no sooner set the ice-cold pitcher of lemonade on the porch when I saw the Blakes' green pickup truck stirring up the dust as it traveled down our rutty road, delivering the members of my girls club. "Ma," I called through the screen door. "Bring out the cookies! The Pretty Pennies are a-coming."

Right away the door opened, but it wasn't Ma. It was my brother Luther wearing a fresh white dress shirt and the blue pants from his Sunday suit. While Susan, Esther, and Bonnie jumped off the truck's back platform, Luther didn't hardly pay no never mind. It wasn't until Ginny the gorgeous climbed down that Luther, wearing a very pleasant expression, took a couple of giant steps toward her and asked, "How y'all getting along, Ginny?"

Ginny didn't get a chance to answer 'cause the one girl who folks say was born into this world talking answered my brother's question. "Fried to a frizzle," said Bonnie Blake. "And that lemonade yonder looks mighty refreshing."

After the lemonade was drunk and the cookies eaten, I performed my duties by rapping on the floor of the porch and saying, "This here meeting of the Pretty Pennies Girls Club is now called to order."

"Trouble with this club," said Bonnie without waiting until we got to new business, "is that we never do nothing but drink lemonade and talk about the boys in the Tiger Hunters' Club."

Heads bobbed up and down in agreement.

Bonnie smiled as though she was onto something big. "What this club needs is somebody with new ideas about things that are fun doing."

Then Ginny did something unusual. She found that one sliver of a moment which Bonnie wasn't cramming with words and said, "We just go from one meeting to the next meeting without ever doing anything. Reckon we could use a new president."

Even before Ginny's words were being applauded, I knew there was some truth to be found in them. We do just sit around gabbing—which is fun—but it was the same amount of fun before I got the idea that we had to become a club. "Philip Hall and the Tiger Hunters ain't the only ones can be a club!" And it was also me that told them how it was a known fact that clubs have more fun than friends. Suddenly I felt ashamed of myself for having promised more than I delivered, but mostly I felt angry with the Pretty Pennies, who were fixing to dump their president without as much as a "begging your pardon."

I looked up at the porch ceiling, looking for something like a good idea waiting to bore through my brain. Well, I looked, but I didn't see nothing but ceiling paint. So I closed my eyes and sure enough something came to me. I waved my hands for quiet. "It so happens that I do have a wonderful idea, but I was waiting to tell y'all about it."

Bonnie began, "Is it fun? 'Cause I got me plenty of chores to do at home so if it's—"

I broke right in. "Quiet! Now next month the Old Rugged Cross Church has their yearly picnic, and I've been thinking that we oughta challenge the Tiger Hunters to a relay race."

"Five of them," said Bonnie. "Five of us."

"Yes siree," I agreed. "But they is going to be something special about our five 'cause we're going to be wearing a special uniform which we ourselves made."

Right away I noticed how all the girls came alive when I mentioned the uniform, so I went on to describe it. "With the money we got in our club treasury, we're going to buy big T-shirts and some different-colored embroidery thread for each Pretty Penny. And then"—my finger traced a crescent across my chest— "we could all embroider the words: THE PRETTY PENNIES GIRLS CLUB OF POCAHONTAS, ARKANSAS." I said, really beginning to feel my presidential powers, "And if we were of a mind to, we could also embroider on the names of all the folks we like."

"You going to embroider on the name of Mister Phil Hall?" asked Bonnie in that cutesy-pooh voice of hers.

I laughed just as though I had nary a worry in this world. Oh, sometimes I think that Philip Hall still likes me, but at other times I think he stopped liking me the moment he stopped being the number-one best everything.

But he wouldn't do that, would he? Stop liking me just because I'm smarter than him? I can't help it and, anyway, my teacher, Miss Johnson, herself said that if I'm going to become a veterinarian I'm going to have to become the best student I know how to be.

On Saturday afternoon all us Pennies went into the Busy Bee Bargain Store for white T-shirts big enough to get lost in. After a lot of discussion, we dropped five T-shirts, fifty skeins of embroidery thread, five embroidery hoops, and five packages of needles onto the wrapping counter in front of Mr. Cyrus J. Putterham.

After taking our money, he pulled one tan sack from the counter and began shoveling everything into it.

"Oh, no, sir," I corrected. "We each need our own bags."

His bushy eyebrows made jumpy little elevator rides up and then down. "Don't you girlies have any feeling? Five sacks cost me five times as much as one."

"But we need them," I explained. " 'Cause we're not even related."

He pulled out four more. "Costs me money, each one does. But you wouldn't care nothing about that. Kids never do!"

As we Pretty Pennies embroidered our shirts on the following Wednesday evening, we drank Bonnie Blake's strawberry soda, ate her potato chips, and gabbed on and on about those Tiger Hunters.

We even sent them a letter saying that they ought to get busy practicing their relay running 'cause we Pretty Pennies were aiming to beat them to pieces.

The next meeting was at Ginny's house, where we all sat in a circle on the linoleum floor and talked about our coming victory over the boys while we munched popcorn from a cast-iron skillet and embroidered away. Then from outside: *Bam . . . bam . . . bam-my . . . bam . . . bam!*

Our embroidery dropped to our laps as we grabbed onto one another. Bonnie pointed toward the outside while, for the first time in her life, her mouth opened and closed and closed and opened without a single sound coming out.

Finally, Esther, who almost never had a word to say, said, "Wha—What was that?"

"Let's see," I said, moving cautiously and pulling Esther along with me toward the door. I peeked out just in time to see two figures (both less than man size) race deeper into the halflight before disappearing from sight.

Bonnie, Ginny, and Susan were still sitting like frozen statues.

"It's OK," I told them. "Whoever they were—and I think I know who they were—have already ran away."

Esther followed me out on the porch, where there was a rock the size of a crow's nest and sticking to this rock was a sheet of wide-lined paper. I pulled off the paper, which had been stuck on with a wad of gum, and read aloud:

> *Dear Pretty Pennies,*
> *You ain't pretty!*
> *You ain't pennies!*
> *And you ain't never going to beat us neither!*
> > *President Philip Hall*
> > *Bravest of all the brave Tiger Hunters*
> > *and Lt. Gordon Jennings (also Brave)*
>
> *P.S. Why wait for the church picnic to relay race? Meet us at the schoolyard on Saturday and we'll win!*

Everybody was really mad and we all began talking at once about those Tiger Hunters who run around scaring the wits out of a person. Bonnie thought we ought to teach them a lesson. "Specially that Phil Hall."

I'd have liked nothing better, but probably for a different reason. It wasn't the scare so much as what he said about not being pretty that ruffled my feathers. Did he mean nobody was pretty? Or was nobody but me pretty? Or . . . or was everybody pretty excepting me? Next thing I knew I was shouting, "We're going to get those low-down polecats!" Then while I had everybody's attention, I gave them their final instructions: "Next Saturday we'll race. Finish embroidering on our club name, front and back. Then everybody wash your shirts so our club name will be clean easy reading. All the folks in Pocahontas is going to know just who it was that beat them Tiger Hunters."

The next morning Philip didn't show up for work at my new business, The Elizabeth Lorraine Lambert & Friend Veg. Stand. Well, he's probably just mad or practicing up his relay running. Or maybe Mr. Hall has him doing chores. But that's the unlikeliest explanation of them all.

Without him there ain't no games or giggles, but today there's not a speck of boredom either 'cause I'm just too busy embroidering my T-shirt and running my business. And with every sale my college money grows. I'm going to become a veterinarian yet.

It was just before bedtime on Friday night that I stitched the last beautiful stitch on my shirt. I held it out for better viewing. Even with the soil from two weeks of handling along with my baby brother Benjamin's mashed-in, smashed-in sweet potato, it was beautiful. Just beautiful!

As I began to draw the wash water, Ma told me to get to bed 'cause I'd be needing my strength for the big race tomorrow. She took the shirt from my hand as she gave me a light shove toward the bedroom. "Reckon I can do the washing if you can do the resting."

When the morning sky came again to Pocahontas, I woke wide awake just as though I hadn't been sleeping at all but only resting up before the big race.

At the kitchen table Ma sat in front of a bowl of peas needing shelling, but her hands sat unmoving in her lap. I tried to remember the last time I had seen my mother just sitting without actually doing anything. All I said was "Morning, Ma," but it was enough to make her look as though she was staring at a spook.

"Reckon I'm going to have to tell you," she said, holding tight to the bowl. "But I don't know how to tell you . . . It's about your shirt. Done shrunk to midget size. Sure did."

As Pa drove down Pocahontas's Main Street, I spotted the rest of the Pennies leaning up against a yellow fireplug. A block away Pa turned his car and angle-parked in front of the E-Z Cash & Carry Market. When the Pennies saw me walking toward them, they all shook their heads just like I was doing something wrong. What does that mean? That I'm not wearing my uniform? No, but I'm carrying it wrapped like a fish in an old newspaper to show them what they'd never believe without seeing. Anyway, they're not wearing theirs either. Too lazy to finish their embroidery probably.

Bonnie began by saying that it was an ordinary washing powder, one of those kinds that they're always talking about over the radio. Then Esther, who would never interrupt anybody, interrupted to say that her water was barely warm.

I was losing patience with everybody talking, everybody understanding but me. "What are you all babbling about mild soap and barely warm water for?"

Suddenly Ginny whipped from a grocery bag a white T-shirt so shrunk that the embroidery's lettering was no longer readable. "We is talking about this."

First we talked about our wasted efforts and then we talked about our wasted money and then we talked about what nobody could understand: what caused the shrinkage.

"Listen here," I said suddenly. "We bought something in good and honest faith that didn't turn out to be a bit of good. Well, if we all go down to the Busy Bee and explain the situation to Mr. Putterham, then he'll give us back our money. Probably even apologize that he can't pay us for our trouble."

"What Mr. Putterham is you talking about?" asked Bonnie, cocking her head like a trained spaniel. "The only Mr. Putterham I know wouldn't apologize to his ma if he ran her down in the broad daylight."

I told her right off. "Trouble with you, Miss Bonnie, is that you ain't got no faith in human nature."

Still, the thought that old bushy eyes ever had a mother was surprising. Reckon I just couldn't see Mr. Putterham having anything that couldn't turn a profit.

ven though I walked into the Busy Bee as slow as I could possibly walk, the others carefully managed to walk even slower. They stayed behind me, pushing me on toward the wrapping counter and the awesome presence of Cyrus J. Putterham. As I watched him tying a piece of string around a shoe box, I got to wishing that one of the other girls had replaced me as president of the Pennies; then they'd be standing here on the firing line instead of me.

The merchant lifted his eyebrows at me, which was a kind of a cheapskate way of asking what I wanted without actually bothering to ask.

"Well, uh . . . Mr. Putterpam—ham! Mr. Putterham, it's uh . . . about what happened two Saturdays ago when we all

bought T-shirts from your store. We washed them like we wash anything else," I said, removing the newspaper from my shirt to hold it up. "And they all five shrunk up like this."

He stretched his lips into a hard straight line. "How much you pay for that shirt?"

"Eighty-nine cents."

"See?"

What did he want me to see? "Sir?"

A short blast of air rushed through his nostrils and I came to understand that his patience zipped off on that blast of air. "Something you girls paid only eighty-nine cents for isn't going to last forever. Why, eighty-nine cents for a T-shirt is mighty cheap."

"Oh, no, sir," I corrected him. "Paying eighty-nine cents for something that ain't never been worn is mighty expensive."

He waved his hand as though he was shooing a fly. "All right, I was nice enough to listen to you girls and now y'all get on out of here. I got me a store to run."

"Yes, sir," I said pleasantly. "We appreciate your attention, sure do. But what we really want is for you to refund us our money 'cause a shirt that ain't fit to be washed ain't fit to be sold."

"Get on out of here!" Both his hands went flapping in the air. "Now get!"

We may have left the store like scared chicks, but once outside we became more like mad wet hens. Esther kept saying, "Imagine!" Or sometimes she'd vary it with "Would you imagine that!"

Then, as if we didn't have enough trouble, the Tiger Hunters led by the bravest of all the brave Tiger Hunters came up to say that we were going to be beaten so bad that it would be a long time before we showed our face in Pocahontas again.

"Don't fret about it," I told him. " 'Cause I don't think I want to show my face anymore, anyway." A warm tear had begun to worm its way down my cheek.

Philip looked uncomfortable. What's the matter? Hadn't he ever seen a tear before? "We don't have to relay race today," he was saying. "We can put it off until the Sunday of the Old Rugged Cross Church picnic."

We shook hands on it, but I was not able to say any more. Talking took too much effort. So Bonnie explained while Ginny showed Philip and his Tiger Hunters what happened to our shirts. Right away Philip said, "We don't have to let Mr. Putterham get away with that. That's robbery!"

Philip's comment about its being a robbery struck me like one of God's own revelations!

At the far end of Main Street, sitting on a square of grass, is the old red brick courthouse where Sheriff Nathan Miller has a narrow office and two barred cells. As the Pennies and Hunters strode up the courthouse walk, old men sitting out on sunny park benches looked up.

The sheriff told us all to crowd on in. "I'll never forget what good police work you and Phil did in capturing those fowl thieves. You know, no farmer has reported any livestock missing since they left town."

His words encouraged me to tell him about our "robbery" at the hands of the merchant Putterham. I watched the sheriff's face grow more and more thoughtful. Finally he said, "I'm sorry, but there ain't no way I can help you out."

" . . . But why?"

With his booted feet, the sheriff pushed his chair from his desk. "Follow me," he said, already walking with strong strides from his office.

Outside, the men on the benches now seemed doubly surprised to see us kids half-running in order to keep up with Randolph County's long-legged lawman. A block down Main Street and then two blocks down School Street to the last house at the end of the block. The sheriff walked up the driveway and into the backyard. At a backyard sandpile a little boy dressed in diapers and pullover shirt toddled over, saying, "Dadadadada."

The sheriff picked him up and then asked me, "What do you think of my boy's shirt?"

Surely eleven folks didn't walk all the way over here just to look at a tight-fitting baby shirt. It seemed silly, but he really did want my opinion. "I reckon it's a nice enough baby shirt," I told him.

"Uh-hun!" answered the more than six feet of sheriff as though he had suddenly struck gold. "Uh-hun," he repeated. "For a baby shirt it's mighty fine, but it wasn't bought to be no baby's shirt. No Sir! It was bought for me. Last Saturday I paid eighty-nine cents for that T-shirt at the Busy Bee Bargain Store."

"You too!!—Then why don't you—"

"Because selling bad merchandise," he said, "can get a merchant in trouble with his customers without getting him in trouble with the law."

We Pretty Pennies walked with the Tiger Hunters back toward Main Street like a bunch of beaten soldiers. No reason for hurrying. No good left in the day nohow. Then it struck me like a pie in the face. Why are we defeated? Ten of us and only one of them Putterhams. "Stop!" I said, whirling around like a general of the army. "We ain't giving up this battle!"

"We ain't?" asked Philip.

I was the fightingest president the Pretty Pennies would ever have. "No, we ain't, 'cause if we all stood out in front of the Busy Bee Bargain Store showing off our shrunken shirts, then old Mr. Putterham would be so embarrassed he'd have to refund our money."

I broke into a run, followed by Philip Hall, followed by the rest of them. In front of the Busy Bee, we all formed a loose line—a Penny, a Hunter, a Penny, and so forth. "Pretty Pennies and Tiger Hunters. When we're working together we'll call ourselves the great Penny Hunters," I said.

Since Philip Hall didn't look exactly thrilled by my suggestion, I said, "Well, would you rather be called the Pretty Tigers?" His groan gave me his answer.

When a heavy woman with three chilluns slowly made her way toward the Busy Bee door, Bonnie approached her. A moment later she was spreading out her doll-size shirt across her chest while the woman shook her head and said, "I'm going to do my trading at Logan's."

The very next person who was persuaded not to spend money at the Busy Bee was my sister, Anne. She said she could buy fingernail polish at the dime store just as well.

After Anne, there was our preacher, the Reverend Ross, who was going to buy some white handkerchiefs from Putterham, but the Reverend said he'd "be happy to respect your picket line."

"Respect our what?" I asked.

"Folks who is standing like some of God's own soldiers against the world's injustices is," said the Reverend Ross, "a picket line."

Never before in my whole life had I ever felt so important, but then never before had I been on special assignment for God.

Just then a family of five reached for the Busy Bee's door and I called out, "Don't you folks go buying things in there unless"—I held up my shirt—"you don't object to shrinking."

"Lordy," said the wife, coming right over to get a closer look. "Now ain't that a pity?"

Mr. Putterham stepped outside the door. "What's this? What's going on here?"

I turned to watch Philip Hall 'cause I didn't want to miss seeing him speak right up to that old man merchant. But the only thing I saw was the bravest Tiger Hunter of them all with his mouth flung open, looking for all the world like he would never again be able to speak.

The proprietor's eyes now swept past Philip and were looking down the long picket line. "Don't tell me that all you kids have been struck speechless? Somebody better tell me what's going on!"

I took one step forward. "I reckon you oughta know that we is picketing your store, Mr. Putterdam—ham! Mr. Putterham."

His big, bushy eyebrows jumped up and down as though they were skipping rope. "You is doing WHAT? And to WHOM?"

"We is"—my mouth felt too dry for stamp licking—"picketing you," I said, grateful that the words actually sounded.

"Now you listen here, you," he said. "Nobody pickets Cyrus J. Putterham, Pocahontas's leading merchant. Know that?"

"Yes, sir."

"Good," he said, smiling a pretend smile. "Then y'all get on out of here."

"Uh . . . no, sir," I said, trying to remember the Reverend Ross's words about being one of God's own soldiers.

"What do you mean No, sir?" he asked, allowing his voice to rise into a full shout. "You just got through saying Yes, sir."

"Uh, well, sir, that was my answer to your question." Mr. Putterham blinked as though my words were being spoken in a strange new language. I tried again. "What I was saying, Mr. Putterjam . . . ham! Mr. Putterham, was yes, sir, I know all about you being Pocahontas's leading merchant. But no, sir, we ain't moving from our picket line. Not until we get our money back."

His eyes told me how much he wanted me to understand. "But if I give you folks your money back, then everybody who ever bought bad merchandise from me will be wanting their money back too."

From the picket line a single voice called, "Give back the money!" Then more voices, more Pennies and Hunters together calling, "Give back the money!" And I joined my voice with the Penny Hunters and even some folks on the

street who were now chanting, *"Give back the money!"* And taken together the voices sounded as though they were doing a lot more demanding than asking.

The shopkeeper threw up his hands. "All right, all right." He smiled, but it wasn't what you'd call a sincere smile. "Making my customers happy is the only thing that's ever been important to Cyrus J. Putterham. Take your shirts back to the wrapping counter for a full and courteous refund."

After all the shirt money was safely back in the hands of our treasurer, Bonnie Blake, I spoke again to the merchant. "There is one more thing, Mr. Putterpam—ham! Mr. Putterham."

"As long as you girls are satisfied—well, that's thanks enough for me. Why, my very business is built on a foundation of square and fair."

"Yes, sir," I agreed. "Would you mind giving us back our embroidery money?"

"Your what?"

I presented him with the cash register receipt. "Two dollars and fifty cents worth of embroidery thread, ruined when our shirts shrunk."

For a moment I thought his face was growing angry, but then he sighed and placed the additional two-fifty on the counter.

"Thanks, Mr. Putterham."

He smiled and this time it didn't look all that insincere. "You called me Putterham. Finally you did it right."

I smiled back at him. "And finally, Mr. Putterham, so did you."

MEET BETTE GREENE, AUTHOR

Like Beth Lambert, the narrator of the story, and Philip Hall in Philip Hall Likes Me. I Reckon Maybe, Bette Greene grew up in a small Arkansas town. As a member of a Jewish family in a town almost entirely populated by Christians, Greene always felt like something of an outsider. Her parents owned and operated the town's general store and were always busy, so Bette was raised mainly by the family's black housekeeper, Ruth.

"I think . . . the thing [that] made me, me, was growing up almost counter to my culture. Growing up Jewish in the middle of the Bible Belt. Being white but having, for all practical purposes, a black mother . . . I became part of both the white culture and the black culture."

The unusual circumstances of Bette Greene's upbringing have undoubtedly influenced the characters and situations she writes about with such sensitivity.

MEET COLIN BOOTMAN, ILLUSTRATOR

Colin Bootman wanted "to capture a feeling of the South and of that time period, the 1940s," in his illustrations for "The Pretty Pennies Picket." He is a native of Trinidad, and, although he has read books about the Deep South, capturing its special character required research at the picture collection of the Manhattan Public Library. In the "Southern Life" collection, he found many pictures of rural general stores to use in illustrating Mr. Putterham's store.

Finding a model for the 1940s vintage pickup truck pictured on page 252 was especially challenging. Bootman first went to a Brooklyn shop that sells vintage trucks but did not find the exact model he wanted. At the Manhattan Public Library he found a picture of just the right model, in just the right position, to guide him in his illustration.

Some artists have a favorite medium. Mr. Bootman prefers to paint his illustrations with oil-based paints.

THE GRIMKÉ SISTERS

from GREAT LIVES:
HUMAN RIGHTS
by William Jay Jacobs
illustrated by Marcy Ramsey

Dignified, serious, dressed simply, with a white hand-kerchief framing her delicate features, Angelina Grimké stood calmly at the speaker's stand, preparing to address a committee of the Massachusetts State Legislature.

Outside the State House, men shook their fists in anger. Some hooted and jeered. Others hissed, not the hisses heard at today's sports events, but hisses born of genuine hatred.

It was Wednesday, February 21, 1838. Until that day no American woman ever had addressed a legislative body in this country. The visitors' gallery was packed to capacity. Standees jammed the aisles and the lobby outside the hall. Many in the crowd had come out of curiosity, just to see a woman speak in public, something then considered shameful, even indecent.

Yet as Miss Grimké's powerful voice rang out across the audience, boldly, magnetically, her listeners riveted their attention on her, gripped by the intensity of her message. For there at the lectern stood a white southern woman, born to wealth and aristocratic position, delivering a passionate attack on the South's "peculiar institution"—human slavery.

"I stand before you as a southerner," she declared, "exiled from the land of my birth by the sound of the lash and the piteous cry of the slave. I stand before you as a repentant slave holder.

"I stand before you," continued Angelina Grimké, "as a moral being, and as a moral being I feel that I owe it to the suffering slave and to the deluded master . . . to do all that I can to overturn a system . . . built upon the broken hearts and prostrate bodies of my countrymen in chains and cemented by the blood, sweat and tears of my sisters in bonds. . . . "

In the audience before her some people openly cried. The chairman of the committee, Miss Grimké later wrote, "was in tears almost the whole time that I was speaking." Sarah, her older sister, was to have been the featured speaker that day. But, ill, she had taken to her bed, persuading young Angelina to substitute for her.

No matter. Before long the names of the two sisters became linked, North and South, as leaders in the forefront of the antislavery movement. Other women, until then hesitant to speak out in public against the curse of slavery, followed their example.

In time the leading women of the age—Lucy Stone, Elizabeth Cady Stanton, Susan B. Anthony—all would express gratitude to the Grimké sisters. It was the Grimkés, they said, who first inspired them to join in battle, crusading for the twin causes of women's rights and the abolition of slavery.

The society into which Sarah and Angelina Grimké had been born could hardly have been a more unlikely setting for the development of social reformers. Charleston, South Carolina, led the South in defending slavery. Wealthy planter aristocrats, including the father of the Grimké sisters, dominated the city's society. The very survival of their gracious and leisurely lifestyle depended on the slave labor system.

It was slaves who planted and harvested their yearly cotton crops—the source of their wealth. It was slaves, too, who built their houses, cooked their meals, cared for their children, stood behind them to fan the flies away as they dined. It was slaves who made possible for the white men their hours of pleasure in hunting and riding, or for the elegant white women the days and evenings filled with tea parties, fancy-dress balls, and an endless round of visits to neighboring plantations.

For young Sarah Grimké, child of the aristocracy, such a life proved, for some reason, not enough to make her happy. Nor did it please the young Angelina, so headstrong, independent, even in childhood, that her mother scarcely could control her. Instead of absorbing the standard school curriculum for girls of the time—music, a touch of French, and gracious manners—the Grimké sisters demanded the right to the same education as their brothers: Latin, Greek, mathematics, philosophy, and law.

Both girls wept at the beatings and other punishments inflicted by slave owners, including even their own parents, to keep blacks humble and obedient. Sometimes Angelina would creep into the slave quarters at night to rub soothing ointment into the open wounds of slaves who had been lashed with the whip.

Sarah, and later Angelina, too, taught the slave girls assigned to them as maids how to read. In most parts of the South such an act was strictly forbidden, but as Angelina admitted with pride in her diary, "The light was put out, the keyhole screened, and flat on our stomachs before the fire, we defied the laws of South Carolina."

In 1819, when Sarah was twenty-seven, her father chose her, instead of his wife or any of her brothers, to travel with him to the North. He was ill and had been advised that a surgeon in Philadelphia might help him, but the illness proved fatal.

The trip was to change Sarah's life. Quakers whom she met in Philadelphia introduced her to their religion. She admired their seriousness of purpose, liked their opposition to slavery. She also approved of the laws passed in Philadelphia to protect free Negroes there.

Although the decision was painful, she decided to leave Charleston and go to live in Philadelphia. Perhaps in the North, she confided to Angelina, a woman might live a life not just of pleasure but of real purpose. In 1829 Angelina, then twenty-four, followed her sister to Philadelphia. Both sisters knew that, hating slavery as they did, the break with their old lives in Charleston could never be healed.

At first the Grimkés tried to live like religious Quakers. They lived simply, dressed simply, and did charity work. But that was not enough for them. Always rebellious, they insisted on speaking aloud in the usually silent Quaker meetings, where they also made a point of sitting in the sections reserved for black women. To them the Quakers were doing too little, moving too slowly, in putting a stop to slavery in America. Just as they had left the Episcopal Church in South Carolina, they also split from the Quakers.

In 1835 Angelina decided to state publicly that all slaves must be freed. She wrote to William Lloyd Garrison, editor of the *Liberator*, America's angriest antislavery newspaper. Abolition of slavery, she declared in her letter, "is a cause worth dying for." Of Garrison himself, she stated that "The ground upon which you stand is holy ground."

Garrison printed Angelina's letter in the *Liberator*. Overnight Angelina and her sister became heroines of the antislavery movement. Here were the daughters of wealthy slave owners daring to describe the brutal acts they personally had witnessed and demanding that the slaves should be freed at once.

Next Angelina wrote a pamphlet, *An Appeal to the Christian Women of the South*, urging white women to join the fight against slavery—to put an end to "this horrible system of oppression and cruelty . . . and wrong," even if they had to break the law.

In Charleston the postmaster publicly burned copies of the pamphlet in the city's main square. Authorities warned Angelina and Sarah not to return home or they would be arrested.

The threat succeeded in keeping the Grimké sisters away from Charleston, but it could not stop them from speaking out. In 1836 Sarah published "Epistle to the Clergy of the Southern States." In that letter she urged southern ministers at least to stop giving their support to slavery, even if they could not offend their congregations by opposing it publicly.

Well known by then, the Grimkés decided to give their lives totally to the abolitionist movement. They joined the American Anti-Slavery Society and began to speak, as a team, to small meetings of women in New York City.

Soon these so-called parlor meetings became so popular that many ministers opened their churches to the Grimké sisters, usually on the condition that no men be present. But before long men demanded the right to hear the lectures, even though the appearance of women as public speakers was considered unwomanly. Almost everywhere, the Grimkés found themselves facing mixed audiences—larger and larger ones as their popularity grew.

It was during their triumphant tour of New England in 1838 that Angelina delivered her famous address to a session of the Massachusetts Legislature in the State House at Boston.

Angelina, tall, with piercing eyes and a strong voice, enjoyed meeting an audience. Sarah, more reserved, did most of the writing for the Grimké team. The two worked well together.

At first William Lloyd Garrison and other leaders of the abolitionist movement pleaded with them not to endanger the antislavery cause by linking it with questions of women's rights, especially the right of women to speak in public. Garrison changed his mind, however, as did Theodore Dwight Weld, who had coached Angelina in techniques of public speaking when she first joined the American Anti-Slavery Society.

Instead of avoiding the issue of women's rights, the Grimké sisters spoke out more strongly on it. They demanded not only the right to be heard, but also the right of women to vote, to help make laws, and even to serve as elected officials. Finally they demanded that women be given complete legal equality with men in such matters as divorce and ownership of property.

At one of their speeches a gang of boys threw apples at them. Spectators jeered at them. Newspapermen dubbed them "the weird sisters," or "Devilina and Grimalkin."

Nothing stopped the Grimkés. In the spring of 1838 they spoke at the Odeon Theater in Boston to mixed audiences of men and women numbering two thousand to three thousand. Clearly they had taken center stage in the antislavery movement. No other women in the country were so well known or so frequently discussed.

By now it became obvious, too, that Theodore Dwight Weld's interest in Angelina went beyond her ideas. He continued to give her lessons in public speaking. He accompanied the Grimkés on their tours. But he also had fallen in love with Angelina—and she with him.

In May 1838 they were married. The wedding party included, in the words of one guest, "a motley assembly of white and black, high and low." In direct defiance of "the horrible prejudice of slavery" the bride and groom introduced as bridesmaids and groomsmen six former slaves from the Grimké plantation. Two white and two black ministers presented prayers. At the end of the ceremony William Lloyd Garrison read the marriage certificate aloud and then passed it around the room to be signed by each guest.

Theodore and Angelina insisted that the wedding cake be made with sugar grown by free laborers. The cotton for their mattress, they proudly pointed out, had come from a farm in New Jersey, not "the usual slave-grown cotton ticking."

Two days after their wedding Angelina and Theodore left for a honeymoon. As might be expected, they spent it working for the antislavery cause. Along with Sarah, they attended the opening session of the Anti-Slavery Convention of American Women, held in Philadelphia's attractive new

Pennsylvania Hall. The hall had been built especially for such occasions, since reformers, even in Quaker-dominated Philadelphia, had experienced difficulty renting space for speeches on such topics as women's rights and abolition.

On the first night of the convention, Angelina Grimké Weld rose to address a mixed audience of more than a thousand blacks and whites. Outside the hall a mob of whites gathered. As Angelina began to speak they shouted and cursed. They stamped their feet. Then they began throwing bricks and stones at the newly opened hall, shattering the windows. Glass fell to the floor, some of it at Angelina's feet.

"What is a mob?" she continued calmly.

What would the breaking of every window be? Any evidence that *we are* wrong, or that slavery is a good and wholesome institution? What if that mob should now burst in upon us, break up our meeting and commit violence on our persons—would this be anything compared with what the slaves endure?

For more than an hour Angelina spoke on as the mob groaned and roared angrily in the background. Nothing could stop her from delivering her message.

Before the meeting could begin on the next night, the mayor of Philadelphia closed the hall, fearing violence. After he left the scene, the mob surged forward. They burst into the offices of the Anti-Slavery Society there and destroyed many precious papers. Then they set fire to the hall, dedicated to free speech, burning it completely to the ground.

In the months that followed the fire Angelina and Theodore Weld did little public speaking. They began to build a family, eventually having three children. Sarah, now alone, came to live with them, first in their home in New Jersey and later in Massachusetts. She took special pleasure in caring for the Weld children.

The three also worked together on an important new collection of documents, *American Slavery As It Is: Testimony of a Thousand Witnesses*. Drawing heavily on advertisements and published accounts in southern newspapers, the study offered powerful evidence against slavery. Included were advertisements for the return of runaway slaves, identified by their owners, for example, as "stamped on the left cheek 'R' and a piece is taken off her left ear, the same letter is branded on the inside of both legs"; or, "branded 'N.E.' on the breast and having both small toes cut off."

Harriet Beecher Stowe relied heavily on the Weld-Grimké evidence in writing *Uncle Tom's Cabin*, the novel that, according to some, became a major emotional cause of the Civil War.

In time, illness and age began to limit the involvement of Sarah, Angelina, and Theodore in the antislavery cause. Still, they continued to circulate petitions against slavery. They also became interested in other reforms of the day, such as less confining clothing for women, sensible diet, and better forms of education.

After the Civil War ended the sisters learned that two of their brother Henry's sons, born of a Negro slave woman, were in the North. Without hesitation they welcomed the boys into their home and paid for their education. One son later became a prominent minister in black churches. The other became a leader in the National Association for the Advancement of Colored People (NAACP).

In 1873 Sarah Grimké died. Six years later Angelina followed her sister to the grave. Both had lived long enough to see the end of slavery in America. And although the women's rights movement had not yet triumphed, the Grimké sisters had been early leaders in drawing the nation's attention to that movement, too.

Women of ability and high character, the Grimkés turned their backs, as young adults, on what surely would have been lives of security, comfort, leisure, and wealth. Instead they chose to live lives of struggle but also of great accomplishment and—through service to others—lives filled with meaning.

I HAVE A DREAM

from the speech by Martin Luther King, Jr.

Born in 1929, Dr. Martin Luther King, Jr., began his career at the age of twenty-seven as the minister of the Dexter Avenue Baptist Church in Montgomery, Alabama. He later became the leader of the struggle for civil rights for African Americans. On August 28, 1963, he made his famous "I Have a Dream" speech in Washington, D.C., where over a quarter-million people were gathered to convince Congress to pass a civil-rights bill. In his speech, Dr. King pleaded for freedom and justice for all people.

So I say to you, my friends, that even though we must face the difficulties of today and tomorrow, I still have a dream. It is a dream deeply rooted in the American dream that one day this nation will rise up and live out the true meaning of its creed—we hold these truths to be self-evident, that all men are created equal.

I have a dream that one day sons of former slaves and sons of former slave-owners will be able to sit down together at the table of brotherhood.

I have a dream my four little children will one day live in a nation where they will not be judged by the color of their skin but by the content of their character. I have a dream today!

I have a dream that one day . . . little black boys and black girls will be able to join hands with little white boys and white girls as sisters and brothers. I have a dream today!

I have a dream that one day every valley shall be exalted, every hill and mountain shall be made low, the rough places shall be made plain, and the crooked places shall be made straight and the glory of the Lord will be revealed and all flesh shall see it together.

This is our hope. This is the faith that I go back to the South with.

With this faith we will be able to hew out of the mountain of despair a stone of hope. With this faith we will be able to transform the jangling discords of our nation into a beautiful symphony of brotherhood.

With this faith we will be able to work together, to pray together, to struggle together, to go to jail together, to stand up for freedom together, knowing that we will be free one day. This will be the day when all of God's children will be able to sing with new meaning—"my country 'tis of thee; sweet land of liberty; of thee I sing; land where my fathers died, land of the pilgrims' pride; from every mountain side, let freedom ring"—and if America is to be a great nation, this must become true.

So let freedom ring from the prodigious hilltops of New Hampshire.

Let freedom ring from the mighty mountains of New York.

Let freedom ring from the heightening Alleghenies of Pennsylvania.

Let freedom ring from the snow-capped Rockies of Colorado.

Let freedom ring from the curvaceous slopes of California.
But not only that.

Let freedom ring from Stone Mountain of Georgia.

Let freedom ring from Lookout Mountain of Tennessee.

Let freedom ring from every hill and molehill of Mississippi, from every mountainside, let freedom ring.

And when we allow freedom to ring, when we let it ring from every village and hamlet, from every state and city, we will be able to speed up that day when all of God's children—black men and white men, Jews and Gentiles, Catholics and Protestants—will be able to join hands and to sing in the words of the old Negro spiritual, "Free at last, free at last; thank God Almighty, we are free at last."

MARTIN LUTHER KING JR.
Gwendolyn Brooks

© Dan McCoy/Black Star

A man went forth with gifts.

He was a prose poem.
He was a tragic grace.
He was a warm music.

He tried to heal the vivid volcanoes.
His ashes are
    reading the world.

His Dream still wishes to anoint
    the barricades of faith and of control.

His word still burns the center of the sun,
    above the thousands and the
    hundred thousands.

The word was Justice. It was spoken.

So it shall be spoken.
So it shall be done.

© Flip Schulke/Black Star

Photos, clockwise from left: © Charles Moore/Black Star, © Charles Moore/Black Star,
© Henri Cartier-Bresson/Magnum, © Bob Adelman/Magnum

MEET GWENDOLYN BROOKS, POET

*Gwendolyn Brooks began submitting poems to an African-American
newspaper when she was sixteen years old. Over seventy-five of her poems
appeared in a column called "Lights and Shadows."*

*"I loved poetry very early and began to put rhymes together
at about seven, at which time my parents expressed most earnest
confidence that I would one day be a writer," she recalled.*

*Gwendolyn Brooks won the Pulitzer Prize in 1950 for
her second book of poetry, entitled* Annie Allen. *She was the first
African American to win a Pulitzer Prize.*

*Most of Brooks's poems are about the everyday life of African
Americans, but her work has something to say to everyone.*

The Uprising. c. 1860. Honoré Daumier.

Conversation. 1909. Henri Matisse.

FINE ART
TAKING A STAND

Horseman with spear. Eastern Han dynasty,
2nd century. Chinese.

Bronze. National Museum, Beijing. Photo: © Erich Lessing/Art Resource

A LONG WAY TO GO

Zibby Oneal
illustrated by Michael Dooling

Lila's nanny, Katie Rose, had Saturdays off. On that day, right after lunch, she went home to help her mother. Sometime, she promised, she'd take Lila along, and one Saturday in September that happened.

First thing in the morning, while she was brushing Lila's hair, Katie Rose said, "How would you like to go home with me today?"

Lila forgot how the brush was pulling her long hair. "Really? Today?" she said.

"I asked your mama and she agreed, if we are sure to be home by supper." All morning Lila squirmed with excitement.

Soon after lunch they set off, Katie Rose prim and pretty in her Saturday hat, and Lila wearing her best coat with the beaver collar. They walked to Fourth Avenue and waited for the trolley. Lila had her fare in her pocket.

"You mustn't expect anything grand," Katie said when they were sitting side by side on the trolley's slippery wooden seat. "We're poor and that's a fact. We all have to help. Delia and Sheila help Mama with her sewing from the shirtwaist factory. Mike sells papers and Annie watches the babies."

Lila nodded. Katie Rose had told her many times about her brothers and sisters, but sometimes Lila got mixed up. There were so many of them.

The trolley rattled along Fourth Avenue, sometimes ringing its bell. Lila looked out the windows to left and right. They rode past rows of shops with striped awnings, past a hotel where a doorman stood holding packages, past a square where fountains were spraying, on and on, starting and stopping. Then the buildings began to look shabbier and the sidewalks became more crowded. Finally Katie stood up. "Next stop's ours." They made their way to the front of the car as the trolley slowed, and climbed down the steep steps when it stopped.

Suddenly they were in a crowd of people. Lila had never seen so many people. "Come along then," Katie Rose said. "It's a bit of a walk from here." She took Lila's hand.

Lila hurried to keep up, trying to look about her as she went. It was like stumbling into a festival or fair. The curbs were lined with pushcarts loaded with every kind of thing for sale—shoelaces and suspenders, bags of potatoes, piles of apples, pillows, pots and pans, barrels of fish. There were huge tin cans full of milk, mounds of shoes, heaps of long underwear. Lila stared. Children were playing in the street, dodging trucks and delivery wagons. Scrawny cats darted under the wheels of carts. Lila had never seen so much going on all at once.

She looked at the tenement buildings along the street and at the fire escapes where laundry was hanging, underwear in plain sight. A woman shook a mop from a window. There was a smell of cooking in the air. The street rang with shouts and laughter. It seemed to Lila that she had never been so far away from home before.

Katie Rose led her across the street toward a dull red building like the others. "Ah, there's Annie," she cried, and Lila saw a girl about her own age on the steps outside the building. She was holding a baby in her arms and watching another, bigger one. "My baby brothers," Katie said as they crossed the street.

Annie lifted the smallest baby onto her shoulder when she saw them coming. She smiled shyly at Lila. "I was hoping Katie Rose would bring you sometime."

Together they went into the building's dark hallway. They climbed a flight of steps and then another. On the third landing, Katie Rose pushed open a door and called, "I'm home! I brought Lila!"

A strong smell of cooking greeted Lila's nose. She blinked, coming in from the darkness of the hallway. In the center of the room was a table where two little girls were sitting with a woman, who Lila guessed, was Katie's mother. All of them were doing something that looked like sewing. "Pulling bastings, are you?" asked Katie Rose. "I told you, Lila, Sheila and Delia help Mama with her sewing. They pull basting threads. And that's Mike over there in the corner."

Before Lila had them sorted out, she was sitting at the table with them, drinking tea. The babies crawled around the legs of the chairs, and the rest of them laughed and told stories. Lila sipped her tea slowly and listened.

"Mike's going to take you out to see the sights, Lila," Katie Rose's mother said.

Lila looked up from her cup. She could see that he didn't want to. "Why doesn't Annie do it?" he muttered.

"You know very well why," said Annie.

"You don't have to take me," Lila said as she followed Mike back down the dark stairway.

"Naw, it's all right." But it didn't sound to Lila as if he really thought so.

"Why couldn't Annie?"

"She's got the babies to mind."

"Can't your mother and Katie do that?"

"Naw, it wouldn't be fair. Mama likes to sit a bit with Katie when she has a chance. Anyway, it's Annie's job, minding them."

"All the time?"

Mike pushed open the outside door and turned to look at her curiously. "After school and weekends," he said, as if he thought anyone would know that.

They stood on the sidewalk in the sunshine. "What d'you want to see?" Mike asked.

"I don't know what there is to see."

"You ever been to the flickers?"

"The what?"

"The motion picture show."

Lila shook her head. Of course she hadn't. Nice people didn't go to places like that, Mama said.

"Want to see one? It costs a nickel."

Lila fingered the change in her pocket. She could feel the smooth edge of a nickel there. All the while she was thinking she shouldn't go, her feet were following Mike down the street.

"Bet you've never seen a nickelodeon," he said. "They're swell. I go there all the time. We could go see a live show. They're swell, too, but they cost more."

The nickelodeon was enough for Lila. At the booth outside the door they paid. Then they went in and found chairs in the darkness. A prickle of excitement ran down Lila's spine as a gray, flickering picture appeared on the screen. Suddenly a train came rushing into view. A cowboy followed on a galloping horse. He waved a gun. The audience yelled. The train went hurtling off a cliff. The audience whistled and stamped on the floor. Then, all at once, nothing. The screen went blank. "Busted," Mike said. "It always happens. But don't worry. You get three reels for a nickel."

Soon the screen flickered again and a picture appeared. A bandit this time. Another chase. Lila stared. She sat without moving until the third reel ended and the lights came on, until Mike said, "It's over."

On the street she stood dazzled by daylight, waiting for whatever would happen next. "I bet you've never been to a penny candy store either," Mike said.

"I haven't."

She had never even imagined one, and she couldn't believe her eyes. In the long glass cases that ran the length of the store, there were gumdrops and jelly beans, jawbreakers, mounds of chocolate-covered cherries, peanuts, and long, thin licorice whips. They walked the whole length of the counter, inspecting the candy, running their fingers along the glass. "Anything costs a penny," Mike said, "but jawbreakers last longest."

Lila felt for pennies in her pocket. She had two, and so she chose a red jawbreaker for herself. Then she chose a green one for Annie because it didn't seem fair that Annie couldn't come.

Mouths full of candy, they wandered out the door. The street was busy as ever, but the slant of the sun had changed. Suddenly Mike's face was serious. "It's time to go get my papers," he said. "I mean the newspapers I sell. It's my job."

"Oh." Lila looked around her, at the alley where a baseball game was going on, at the bunch of boys pitching pennies on the sidewalk, at the horse-drawn ice wagon coming down the street. She sniffed the warm odor of sugar floating through the candy store door. She had never been any place that was so exciting. But now it was about to end. Mike was going off to sell his papers. Soon she and Katie Rose would take the trolley home and she would have supper in the nursery and play next day in the fenced-in park and remember not to dirty her dress.

"You better go stay with Annie now," Mike said. "I'll show you the way."

But she didn't want to go back. She didn't want it all to end. "Can't I come with you?"

"Naw, girls can't."

"Why can't they?"

"Girls don't sell papers."

"Why not?"

"They're too weak." Mike pretended to be holding up the hem of a skirt. "They're too del-i-cate."

Lila stuck out her chin. "I'm not."

"Sure you are. All girls are." He looked at her and grinned.

Lila didn't plan what happened next. It just seemed to happen. One minute Mike was grinning at her, and the next he was holding his jaw.

"What'd you hit me for?" he asked.

"Because of what you said." Lila didn't really know. Maybe she had hit him to show him she wasn't weak.

"What did I say?" He looked puzzled.

"That girls are weak and delicate."

"But it's true." She could see that he really believed it was true, that he hadn't meant to insult her. She didn't care. She was tired of hearing things like that.

"I could sell papers as well as you," she said. "Any girl could."

"You couldn't even carry them."

"I could!"

Mike was stroking his jaw as if it still hurt him. He looked at her. "Yeah?" he said. "Well, come on and try then."

Lila counted more than thirty newsboys waiting to pick up their papers outside the office building where she and Mike stopped. A man was dumping great rope-bound bundles onto the sidewalk. "You wait here," Mike said and hurried into the crowd. In his cloth cap and knickers he looked just like every other boy waiting there. Lila soon lost sight of him.

She stood on the sidewalk, feeling out of place in her Sunday coat and white hair bow—the only girl on the street. Maybe this is a mistake, she thought. But then she thought again. She remembered the yellow chrysanthemum, the flower the suffragists wore, pressed in a book in her room at home. She remembered Grandmama striding off so proudly to speak. Of course she could sell papers!

In a few minutes, Mike was back, carrying a canvas bag on his shoulder. "Go ahead, take some," he said, "since you're so strong." He handed Lila the bag, half full.

Her shoulder sagged under the weight. "Heavy, aren't they?" Mike said.

Lila shrugged. "Not very."

She didn't think that he believed her. "Come on, then. I sell on the corner of Tenth Street," he said.

Lila tried to hurry. The strap of the bag cut into her shoulder, and the weight of it bumped against her hip, but she didn't intend to let that slow her down. She walked as fast as she could.

"The headlines aren't much good today," Mike said. "What I like is when there's a murder or the Germans torpedo a ship.

That's when you really sell papers. All we got today is some speech about Liberty Bonds and a fire in a warehouse in Brooklyn." He shrugged. "So I'll have to use my imagination. That's what you do when the headlines aren't much. It's like advertising. Nobody's going to want to read the bond speech, of course, so I guess I'll have to work on the fire."

Lila didn't see how he could talk so much carrying papers. She could hardly breathe. Her shoulder ached and her arm was going numb. But of course she didn't say so. She wouldn't say so if she had to walk another five miles. She bit her lip and kept going.

Then, just when she thought she couldn't carry the papers much longer, when her arm felt dead as a stick of wood, they stopped. "This is it," said Mike. "My corner." He dropped most of his papers onto the sidewalk. Gratefully Lila dropped hers.

"Now let's see you sell," Mike said, but he didn't wait to watch. Instead he began running after customers, waving papers, shouting "Read all about the big fire in Brooklyn! Read about the flames forty feet high!"

Lila pulled a paper from the bag and looked at it. She couldn't see where he was getting all that. The paper didn't say a thing about flames. It didn't really say much about the fire. That was what he meant by imagination, she guessed, but it didn't seem quite fair to fool people that way.

She ran her eyes down the front page. The bond speech. The fire. But then she saw, down at the bottom of the page, not taking much space, a small article headed, SUFFRAGISTS REFUSE TO EAT. Lila read as fast as she could. There were suffragists in jail in Washington who wouldn't eat a bite. They said they'd rather starve than do without the vote. The paper called it a hunger strike.

Lila's eyes widened. This was news. This was something interesting. And, besides, it was true. She pulled a few more papers from her bag and stood herself right in the middle of the sidewalk. "Suffragists starving to death!" she yelled. "Read all about it!"

To her amazement, someone stopped to buy a paper. She tried again. "Read all about the ladies starving to death in Washington!" And, again, someone stopped.

"Crazy women," the man said, but he paid her and didn't seem to think it was strange at all to see a girl selling papers.

Lila felt encouraged. Over and over she waved her papers at people walking past. She shouted her headline until she was hoarse but it felt good to be hoarse, to be shouting and running.

"President making women starve!" she cried. "They won't eat till they get to vote!" Anything she said seemed to work. People bought papers. Maybe they would have bought them anyway, thought Lila. She didn't know, but she didn't care. She was too busy selling. In no time, her bag was empty.

She hadn't had time to think about Mike, but now, bag empty, she turned around to look for him. He was leaning against a lamppost, watching her. "I sold them all," she said breathlessly.

"I noticed."

"Here's the money." She fished the change and a few bills from her pocket.

"You keep it."

"No. Why?"

"You earned it."

"But I didn't do it for that." Lila thought of Annie, minding the babies, of the little girls pulling basting threads all afternoon. "You take the money. I just did it to show you I could."

"Yeah. Well." Mike kicked the lamppost with the toe of his shoe. "I guess you showed me."

There were things that Lila felt like saying, but she decided not to say them. Instead she picked up the empty canvas bag and slung it over her shoulder. Together they started back the way they had come.

It was twilight. The streets were filled with the sounds of horns and engines. Lights blossomed in shop windows. People hurried along the sidewalk. On a corner, leaning against the side of a parked truck, a man was playing a harmonica. "Over There," he played slowly, making the notes sound like a sleepy bugle call. "Over There." It was a tune Katie Rose sometimes sang when she was folding laundry, thinking about her sweetheart overseas. The music sounded soft and sad in the twilight.

The two of them walked on in silence, and the mournful notes of the harmonica followed after them. Lila felt too tired to talk. Her head swam with new things to think about—the candy store with all its treasures, the nickelodeon with its flickering screen, the pushcarts loaded with things to sell, the sounds and smells of this new neighborhood. But most of all it was selling papers that she wanted to remember—running after customers, yelling her headlines. The canvas bag swung against her shoulder. She smiled.

The men who sold goods from the pushcarts were packing up when the two of them turned the corner onto Mike's street. Lila could see Katie Rose standing on the steps at the end of the block, and she knew they should hurry, but instead she slowed down.

"I'm sorry I hit you," she said.

"Yeah, well, I'm sorry for what I said about girls."

"You just didn't know any better."

"I never saw a girl selling papers before." Then he turned to look at her and Lila thought that he looked shy. "You were good at it," he said. "You knew what to do."

Lila smiled and handed him the canvas bag and they went on down the street.

So now it was really over—the wonderful afternoon. Now she would go home with Katie Rose and turn into a proper little girl again. It was like the end of a fairy tale, Lila thought. Except it was sad.

On the trolley she leaned against Katie Rose and closed her eyes. It was over. Lila thought, but she would remember, and a memory, like a jawbreaker, lasted a long, long time.

"And then," said Lila on Sunday morning, bouncing on Grandmama's bed. "And then—"

"And then Katie Rose brought you home."

"Yes."

"Lila, you've told me all about it three times."

She had. She couldn't help it. Saturday afternoon was like a story she didn't want to finish, like a book of beautiful colored pictures that she couldn't bear to close.

"Oh, I liked it all so much, but I'm not going to tell anyone else about it. Just you." Lila looked out the window at the sunlight on the fence around the park. "I wish girls could sell papers," she said a little sadly. "I mean all the time."

"There are more and more things that girls can do. Think of all the jobs women have now that there's a war on. When I was your age we didn't dream of working in offices and factories."

"That's women. I mean girls." And then, "Do you think that if women could vote, they'd let girls sell papers?"

Grandmama laughed. "I don't know. I suppose there'd be a better chance of that happening."

"Then I'm a suffragist," Lila said. "I *thought* I was, but now I'm sure."

"That's fine."

Lila frowned. "But what can I do?"

"Believe that women have rights the same as men."

That wasn't what Lila had in mind. She wanted action. She wanted to shout headlines, run around yelling. "I could give speeches," she said. She imagined herself standing on a wooden box speaking to crowds in the street. It would be a lot like selling papers.

But Grandmama only laughed again. "You're still too young to make speeches."

"But I want to do *something*. It's no use just sitting around believing things."

Grandmama looked thoughtful. "Well, there's a suffragist parade a week or so before the state election. We're going to march up Fifth Avenue all the way from Washington Square to Fifty-ninth Street."

"With signs?" said Lila. "And banners?"

"Oh, yes, and music, too. We're going to make people notice us."

"Would you take me?"

"Well, I was thinking—"

Lila sat up straight. "I'm coming."

"But not without permission you aren't. Not unless your mama and papa agree."

"I'll make them agree," said Lila, though she had no idea how she'd do that.

"Well, I'll try to help you," Grandmama said. "At least I'll mention the parade."

Lila sat quietly in church with her hands in her lap. She played nicely with her brother George until lunchtime, rolling his ball to him over and over though this was the most boring game in the world. She sat straight at the table and ate all her lunch, though that included beets. Really, Lila thought, she was being so perfect it was hard to see how Mama and Papa could say no.

But that was what Papa said. While they were waiting for dessert, Grandmama brought up the parade. She did it in a kind of offhanded way, as if it were something she'd only just remembered. "And I think Lila would like to march, too," she said. Lila looked down at her napkin and crossed her fingers. But Papa said no.

It was such a small word, no, but it seemed to Lila that it was the biggest word in her life. So many nos. She felt tears of disappointment prickling in her eyes. She couldn't look up.

When, after lunch, Papa said, "Come on, Lila, it's time for our Sunday walk," Lila felt like saying, "No!" She didn't want to go for a walk with her father. She felt too mad and disappointed. All the same, she went to get her coat, because a little girl didn't say no to her father.

"Which way shall we walk?" he asked her when they were standing on the pavement.

"I don't care." And she didn't. She didn't care at all.

"What about Fifth Avenue then?"

Lila had known he'd choose that. Papa liked walking along Fifth Avenue, looking at the new motorcars pass by. One day, he said, he thought he might buy one.

And so they walked over to Fifth Avenue. Lila was wearing her best coat again and clean white gloves because Papa liked her to look like a lady when they went walking. But her hands felt crowded in the gloves and her shoulders felt crowded in her coat. She felt crowded all over.

At the corner of Fifth Avenue, they turned and walked north, past banks and office buildings, past shops and department stores. Usually Lila liked looking into the department store windows, but today they didn't seem exciting. She thought of the pushcarts on Katie Rose's street. Fifth Avenue was dull.

"Has the cat got your tongue?" Papa said.

"No. I'm thinking."

"About important things?"

"I was thinking about the parade. It's going to come right up this street."

"Lila, you must forget the parade."

But how could she? She couldn't stop thinking about it, even though the thinking made her sad.

They waited to cross the street while a car passed. "That's a Pierce Arrow," Papa said. "It's really something, isn't it?"

Lila nodded. She supposed so.

"Maybe when George is older we'll buy one like that. He can learn to drive it."

"What about me?"

"Oh, you'll be a beautiful grown lady by then. You can ride in the back and tell George where to take you. You'll have all kinds of pretty clothes to wear. We'll go shopping for things like the dress in that window."

Lila glanced at the dress in the shop window. She had to admit it was pretty. She wondered why she didn't like it more, and then she knew. It looked like the kind of dress that was for sitting around doing nothing.

"I'd rather learn how to drive a motorcar," she said, "I'd rather be *doing* something."

Papa didn't understand. "There'll be plenty for you to do. Tea dances and parties and all that sort of thing."

"Those aren't the things I want to do."

"No? What then?"

"Oh!" Lists of things came tumbling into Lila's head. She wanted to march in the parade, turn cartwheels, walk on her hands, roll her stockings down. She wanted to run and yell, sell papers—but that was not what Papa meant. He meant later, when she was grown-up. What did she want to do *then*? Lila closed her eyes and squeezed them tight. "I want to vote," she said.

The words were out before she knew she was going to say them, but suddenly they seemed just right. "I want to be able to vote same as George."

When she opened her eyes, Papa was looking at her. "That's what you want more than anything?"

Lila nodded. She dug her fists into her pockets and looked up at Papa bravely. "It's what Grandmama says. Girls are people, too. They have rights. It isn't fair the way it is. Billy Ash says he's smarter than me just because he's a boy. But I'm the one who gets all A's, not him. So why should he be allowed to vote and not me? Why should George if I can't? It's not fair, Papa. It's not fair to girls."

Lila paused for breath, but she couldn't stop talking. "When I grow up, I want to be just like Grandmama. I want to make things fair for everyone. That's why I want to march in the parade—to show people that's what I think. And if they put me in jail for marching, then I just won't eat, like the ladies in Washington."

Then Lila stopped. She didn't have anything else to say.

"Well," said Papa, "that was quite a speech."

Lila couldn't tell what he was thinking. His face was very serious. She wondered if he would stop loving her now because of all she'd said. She wondered if he'd already stopped. She waited for him to say something more, but he said nothing at all. He took her hand and they went on walking.

Lila's feet slapped along beside him. It was too late now to take it back, and, anyway, she couldn't take it back without lying. She'd said what she meant. But Papa wasn't saying anything at all. He was looking straight ahead as if he had forgotten all about her, as if he didn't know she was there anymore.

Lila felt hollow in the middle. She bit the insides of her cheeks to keep from crying. On the way home, she counted cracks in the sidewalk.

When they reached the corner of Twenty-first Street and were almost home, Papa said, "How did you happen to know about those women in Washington, the ones who aren't eating? Did Grandmama tell you?"

Lila shook her head, still counting cracks. "No," she said. "I read it in the paper."

"Did you really? For heaven's sake." Lila could have sworn, if she hadn't known better, that he sounded proud of her.

After supper, she had her bath and watched Katie Rose laying out her clothes for school the next day. The same old stockings. The same old dress. Lila sighed. Everything was the same old thing again, except that now it would be different with Papa. She climbed out of the tub and wrapped herself in a towel. She went into her room to put on her nightgown.

And that was when Grandmama came in. She had a funny, puzzled sort of expression. "It looks as if we'll be going to the parade together," she said.

Lila paused. The damp ends of her hair swung against her shoulders. "What?"

"Your father says you may go."

"With you? To the parade?" Lila felt as if she couldn't take it all in so fast.

"That's what he says."

"But why?"

Grandmama shrugged. "I don't know what you said to him on that walk, but you must have said something."

Lila swallowed. He had called it a speech. She had made a speech and he'd listened! A bubble of happiness began to rise inside her. He had listened and it was all right. She grinned at Grandmama. She dropped her towel. And then right there, in the middle of her bedroom, she turned a cartwheel.

There were weeks of waiting before the parade. October crawled by like a snail. Lila imagined marching a hundred times before, at last, the day arrived, the special Saturday.

She woke in a shiver of excitement. She could hardly hold still while Katie Rose braided her hair. "You button your shoes yourself," Katie Rose said. "I can't manage with so much wiggling." And she handed Lila the buttonhook.

"Will you be sure to remember to tell Mike that I'm marching?"

Katie Rose snorted. "Do you think I could forget? You remind me every day."

Lila laughed. She was hoping that maybe—just maybe—Mike would come out to watch the parade.

"And tell Annie I wish she could march, too," Lila said. "Tell her I'm marching for her."

And then she jumped up and started downstairs because she couldn't hold still for more than a minute.

Grandmama was in the parlor, reading the paper. "I'm ready!" Lila cried.

Grandmama looked up. "That's fine, but you'll have a bit of a wait. The parade won't begin for several hours."

Lila twirled on the piano stool. She practiced marching between the parlor windows. Grandmama rattled the paper. "President Wilson has come to his senses, I see. He says he wishes our cause godspeed."

"What does that mean?" asked Lila.

"It means he wishes us luck. He's changing his spots, I think, just like your papa."

"What does *that* mean?"

"He's changing his mind. It says here he's leaning toward a constitutional amendment."

"So maybe there won't *be* a parade?"

"Of course there'll be a parade. We haven't *got* the amendment yet."

Lila let out her breath, relieved. She wondered how to spend the next few hours.

When at last they set out for the parade, Mama stood in the parlor window waving. Lila skipped and whirled up the sidewalk. They were going to catch a cab at the corner.

The cab dropped them a block from Washington Square. Lila could hear snatches of music as they walked toward it. "Those are the bands warming up," Grandmama said. "There's going to be a lot of music."

Lila trotted along beside her. The music grew louder and louder. And then they were in Washington Square, and Lila's eyes opened round as saucers.

There were women everywhere, hundreds and hundreds of them. Some carried flags, some were unrolling banners with words printed on them. There were women dressed in nurses' uniforms, women in Red Cross costumes, women wearing yellow chrysanthemums in their hats. So many women! There were old women, young women, white women, black women. There was even a woman standing in line propped on crutches.

"How can she march on crutches?" Lila whispered.

"She can if she makes her mind up to do it," Grandmama said. "That's what this is all about."

"Line up! Line up!" someone was shouting. A bass drum boomed. Grandmama took Lila's hand and they slipped quickly into line.

And then the music began. All at once, all the bands were playing and the columns of women began to move. Left, left. Lila was marching. Above her, the yellow banners streamed.

Out of Washington Square they marched and onto Fifth Avenue. Before and behind came the sound of the drums, and the flags snapped in the breeze. Left, left. On they went up the street, marching in time to the music.

From the curbs came the sound of whistles and cheers. Yellow streamers flew from the shop doors. White-gloved policemen held back the crowds as the bands and the marchers passed.

Lila felt she could march forever, her feet in step with the drums. Back straight, chin up. Left, left, left.

Just as they were crossing Tenth Street, it happened. The bands were playing "Over There." People on the sidewalk were shouting. Lila was looking into the crowd—just in case maybe—when something splashed at her feet.

It splashed and then it splattered red pulp and yellow seeds all over her stockings, all over the hem of her coat. "Someone threw a tomato!" she cried. "Someone threw it right at me!" She tugged Grandmama's hand. There were tears in her eyes.

Grandmama looked down. "Never mind. Just keep marching."

"But, Grandmama, a tomato! It's all over my legs!"

"These things happen sometimes, Lila. It is part of doing what we're doing. There are lots of people who don't want us to vote, lots who don't like this parade. Now be a brave girl. Show them they can't stop you. Keep marching."

Lila thought she was going to cry. Her feet kept moving, but she had lost step. She looked down at the red juice all over her white stockings. And then she got mad. She stuck out her chin and looked straight ahead, and her feet began to move in time with the music.

Left, left. A tomato couldn't stop her. She thought about the woman on crutches. She thought of the women who were still in jail in Washington and about the ones who weren't eating. She thought of all the speeches that Grandmama had made. She thought of her own speech to Papa. She remembered Annie minding the babies and Sheila and Delia pulling bastings all day Saturday. A tomato wasn't much, she thought. A tomato was nothing.

Head up, looking straight ahead, Lila marched on, her feet keeping time with the music.

By the time the parade reached Twenty-first Street, Lila's stockings were dry. The bands were playing "Tipperary." Lila knew the words to that song. She knew they talked about a long way to go. She began to sing to herself as she marched along.

And then Grandmama began singing. And soon women all around them had taken up the song. They sang about what a long way there was to go, and it seemed to Lila that those words meant a lot to them.

Then, suddenly, Grandmama squeezed her hand. "Look, Lila! Look who's waving!"

Lila turned. There on the curb were Mama and Papa, and George in his carriage. Lila waved. Then the parade swept her on. She wondered whether Papa had noticed her stockings.

"Imagine your papa coming out for this parade!" Grandmama leaned over and hugged her. "You know, something tells me we're going to win! One of these days we'll be voting."

They marched on, past the reviewing stand. They marched until Lila's legs felt like stumps. They marched while the sun slid down in the sky and disappeared behind buildings.

It was twilight by the time the parade broke up and Grandmama said, "Let's go home in a cab." Lila was glad to hear that. She didn't feel like walking.

While they waited for a taxi, Lila looked down at her tomato-splattered stockings. She felt proud of them. They were like a badge. She didn't even think of rolling them down.

ABOUT THE WOMEN'S SUFFRAGE MOVEMENT

In 1848, Elizabeth Cady Stanton and Lucretia Mott met at Seneca Falls, New York, to draw up a declaration of women's rights. Now, the idea that women have rights is taken for granted. Then, it was not. Women had few rights and certainly not the right to vote. In their declaration, Mrs. Stanton and Mrs. Mott asked for that.

Both these women were abolitionists who worked before the Civil War for the freeing of slaves. Human rights included women's rights, they thought. If Negroes were freed and allowed to vote, couldn't women expect the same? It didn't work that way. After the Civil War, Congress passed the Fourteenth Amendment to the Constitution, permitting all citizens to vote, providing they were male! The women who had worked so hard for abolition were outraged.

In 1890, they formed the National American Woman Suffrage Association. Mrs. Stanton was its first president and working with her was another important woman in the suffrage movement, Susan B. Anthony. Together they were determined to win votes for women.

For the next thirty years, suffragists worked tirelessly. They collected signatures on petitions, traveled great distances to speak about suffrage, visited Congress and the president many times with their request. Over and over, they were turned down. Both President Woodrow Wilson and most members of Congress felt that women's suffrage was a matter to be decided by the individual states and not by a change in the Constitution. They were supported by numbers of men—and many women—who opposed women's right to vote at all. Finally, in frustration, the suffragists decided to begin picketing the White House.

This same year, 1917, the United States entered the First World War. American troops were sent to Europe to help England and France in their war with the Germans. Women's suffrage was not the main topic on the minds of the men in government. But the suffragists worked on.

In November 1917, New York finally joined other states in granting women the right to vote. This was a turning point. Members of Congress began to see that pressure for a constitutional amendment was enormous. President Wilson gave it his support, and in 1919 the Senate voted in favor.

In August 1920, the Nineteenth Amendment was finally ratified by two-thirds of the states, and after seventy years of trying, women had won the right to vote.

GANDHI

Nigel Hunter
illustrated by Richard Hook

His face is familiar to people in all parts of the world, but to the people of India, Mahatma Gandhi is part of the landscape itself. In every Indian town and village, you are likely to see his image. It could be a framed portrait in the Post Office or bank or a faded photograph displayed on the crumbling wall of a back street tea shop. It could be a brightly-colored postcard clipped to the side of a street-vendor's stall; or a full-length statue set up in the restful shade of a public park or above the hurly-burly and bustle of the crossroads.

He may be pictured at his spinning wheel, absorbed in concentration, or playing with children, laughing good naturedly. Or perhaps he is drinking tea with the Viceroy. More often, he is portrayed striding purposefully forward, leading the movement for Indian independence; for freedom, peace and friendship. Millions affectionately called him *Bapu,* father of the nation. As a sign of respect he became known as Gandhiji and was also called "Mahatma" (great soul) by one of India's finest poets, Rabindranath Tagore.

Gandhi with his granddaughters in New Delhi.
Popperfoto

People in every part of India remember Gandhi. In the southern town of Madurai, what was once a palace is now a museum dedicated to his memory. Outside, in reconstructed buildings, his modest *ashram* living conditions are shown. Inside, a display of words and pictures portrays the long, painful, triumphant march to freedom from British rule. Behind glass there are relics of Gandhi's life; photographs, letters, documents and books; a pair of spectacles, and a spinning wheel. In one cool and carefully-lit space lies an exhibit that bears witness to his sudden, shocking death: a quantity of simple homespun-cloth, white linen darkened by the stain of blood . . .

A HINDU FAMILY

When Mohandas Gandhi was born in 1869, the British Empire was at the peak of its power. The British had ruled India for almost three centuries. Certain parts of the country, ruled by princes who were loyal to the British, were allowed to continue as separate princely states. Mohandas' father was the *Diwan*, or Prime Minister, of Porbandar, a small princely state on India's western coast. It was an appointment that passed from father to son.

His first language was Gujarati; his family's religion was Hindu.

When he was thirteen, his parents arranged for him to marry. In later life, he criticized the custom of child-marriage, but at the time he readily accepted it. Mohandas' bride,

Gandhi's wedding. His head is covered with traditional decorations.

Kasturbai, was also thirteen, and he soon became devoted to her. He was a very strict husband, and Kasturbai felt he restrained her too much. She was supposed to get his permission before seeing her friends, or visiting the temple. Firmly, she resisted, until he grew to accept her point of view. It was a valuable lesson to Mohandas: he learned that nonviolent persuasion could convince people that they were wrong. Years later, nonviolent resistance would prove to be a powerful weapon in the struggle for social and political reform.

WIDENING HORIZONS

Gandhi's family hoped that he might become a *Diwan*, like his father and grandfather before him. For this, it would be a great advantage for him to study law in England, and so he sailed from Bombay in September 1888. For nearly three years, he would be away from Kasturbai, who had just given birth to a son.

Gandhi was ill at ease in Britain at first. He had very little confidence but studied English manners, dressed expensively, and took dancing lessons, trying to fit into English society as a gentleman. While living in London, Gandhi first read the *Bhagavad Gita,* the greatest holy book of Hinduism. As a boy, he had known some of the Hindu stories, but had not held any particular religious beliefs. He had developed friendships with people of many different religions. This helped him to develop a respect for different religions, but he remained uncommitted to any particular faith. Both the *Bhagavad Gita,* and then the Christian *New Testament,* had a profound effect on him.

As soon as he had qualified in law, Gandhi returned home to India. At first, prospects as a lawyer were uncertain because of his nervousness in public. Then a chance came to work on a business dispute in South Africa. This changed his life.

THE CHALLENGE

Soon after his arrival in South Africa, while traveling to the city of Pretoria, Gandhi was forcibly ejected from a first-class train compartment. This was simply because he was Indian and the South African whites assumed that he had no right to enjoy first-class train travel. He spent the night on the station platform, considering the humiliations that the Indians in South Africa suffered daily.

Ninety thousand Indians lived and worked in South Africa under white British rule, often in appalling conditions, and many were treated almost as slaves. Only a few hundred Indians, who owned a large amount of land, enjoyed the right to vote in the South African government. For all the Indians, government restrictions were a way of life.

Gandhi is ejected from a first-class train seat because he is Indian.

Continuing his journey to Pretoria, Gandhi faced more insults. On a stagecoach, he was again shocked that he was not allowed to take a place inside the coach. He was then beaten by the driver for refusing to sit on the footboard, outside the carriage.

The journey to Pretoria spurred him into action. In the face of this racial injustice, Gandhi lost his public timidity and called a meeting to discuss the Indians' situation. From this, an organization emerged through which Indians could voice their discontent. Within a short time, Gandhi was acknowledged as a leader of the South African Indian community.

Meanwhile, the legal case that had originally brought Gandhi to South Africa was successfully resolved, largely through his own contribution. His method of solving the dispute was to appeal to what he called "the better side of human nature." To Gandhi, the point was not to achieve outright victory for one side over the other, but to bring both sides together in a mutually satisfactory arrangement. Before long, he was a highly successful lawyer.

It was at this time that Gandhi developed a belief that God was "absolute truth" and that the way to reach Him was through the concept of nonviolence.

TOWARD COMMUNITY

Over the next twenty years, Gandhi was to lead the Indians of South Africa in their struggle for justice and equality. He developed a form of political struggle based on nonviolent civil disobedience.

In 1894, Gandhi organized a successful petition and newspaper publicity against new anti-Indian laws. He helped to set up the Natal Indian Congress, which aimed to improve life for the Indian community through educational, social and political work. Gandhi returned to his family in India, and there he publicized the injustices in South Africa and sought support to tackle the problems. When he returned to South Africa he was brutally attacked for being a troublemaker by a white mob. As he recovered at a friend's house, a crowd gathered menacingly outside and sang "We'll hang old Gandhi on the sour apple tree . . ." He managed to escape under the cover of night, disguised as a policeman, and said that he forgave his attackers.

During the Boer War (1899–1902) between Britain and the South African Boers, Gandhi formed and led the Indian Ambulance Corps, which worked for the British Army. Since he was demanding rights as a citizen, he felt he owed loyalty to the British Empire; and Britain awarded him a medal. After the war he visited India again, and renewed his contacts with the leaders of the country's growing nationalist movement.

On his return to South Africa in 1903, Gandhi started a magazine for Indians in South Africa. It was called *Indian Opinion*, and it became crucial to the campaign for equality. His lifestyle changed. He decided to give up all his possessions and established a community. Here, he detached himself from his normal family ties. Gandhi believed that to serve others, he must not distract himself with the burden of possessions or involvement with family and the pleasures of family life.

A new law in South Africa required all Indians over eight years old to register with the authorities, and carry a pass at all times. Failing this, they could be imprisoned, fined, or deported. Under Gandhi's leadership, the Indians resisted this new law. He called their action *satyagraha*, which means "holding to the truth." They would not cooperate with the authorities and their resistance was to be nonviolent. Courageously, they confronted prison, poverty, hunger, and violence against them, peacefully refusing to obey the law.

Smuts confronts the prisoner Gandhi.

In 1908, Gandhi visited London to muster support. On his return to South Africa, he was imprisoned. Still wearing prison uniform, he was taken to meet General Jan Christiaan Smuts, the South African leader. Smuts promised that if the Indians registered, he would repeal the registration law. Trusting him, Gandhi called on all Indians to register. But Smuts broke his word. In protest, Gandhi led a public burning of the registration certificates. The campaign continued, with thousands of Indians inviting arrest by refusing to register.

Gandhi spent much of his time in prison reading and writing. He discovered the works of the famous Russian writer Leo Tolstoy, and, inspired by each other's ideas, they began exchanging letters. With the help of a friend, Gandhi founded a new community called *Tolstoy Farm*. The community members grew their own food, made their own clothes and built their own homes. Gandhi himself baked bread and made marmalade, and helped to teach the children.

More new laws, including one that said only Christian marriages were legal, prompted Gandhi to step up his campaigning. Again and again he was jailed, along with thousands of others. Many people were assaulted by the police, and several died. Finally, on the main issues, Smuts gave way. With this vital experience behind him, Gandhi was ready to return to India.

AN INDIAN FUTURE

In Bombay in 1915, Gandhi was welcomed as a hero. He no longer wore western clothing, and he chose to speak Gujarati rather than English, as English was the language of the oppressor. For a year, he toured the country, speaking

Gandhi toured India, talking to the people.

on religious and social matters. He visited the community that had been started by the poet Rabindranath Tagore. Tagore shared many of Gandhi's ideals. He compared Gandhi to Buddha, because like Gandhi, he had also taught the importance of kindness to all living creatures. Outside the city of Ahmedabad, Gandhi founded the *Satyagraha Ashram*, a community committed to nonviolence and service to others.

Gandhi was determined to break down the Hindu "caste" system, which prevented the caste of Hindus who traditionally did the dirtiest work, from ever entering temples. They were called the "untouchables" because their mere touch horrified higher class Hindus. Despite opposition from Kasturbai and others who found it hard to accept, he brought an "untouchable" family into the *Ashram* and renamed them *Harijans*, meaning "Children of God."

Gandhi successfully led the workers of the province of Bihar in a nonviolent campaign against the unjust demands of British landowners. He carried out a fast, threatening to starve himself to death unless his demands were met. His action resulted in better wages and conditions for mill workers. He also inspired farm workers who were suffering the effects of famine not to pay Government tax demands, and eventually the demands were withdrawn. He always appealed to his opponents' sense of right and wrong. Briefly, during World War I (1914–18), he helped to recruit Indian soldiers for the British Army. This seemed at odds with his belief in nonviolence; but he hoped that service to save the Empire would earn India self-rule after the war. However, Britain passed harsh new laws preventing India from becoming a self-governing country within the Empire.

When Gandhi heard about the new British laws, preventing Indian Home Rule, he called on all Indians to suspend business for a day of national, nonviolent protest, including fasting, prayer and public meetings. But troops in Delhi killed nine people, and when Gandhi tried to reach the city, he was arrested and turned back. News of this provoked rioting and violence in several places. It seemed to Gandhi that he had made a grave mistake. People still did not understand that *satyagraha* persuasion should be nonviolent. He punished himself by fasting for three days.

Then came the terrible massacre at Amritsar. On April 13, 1919, about 15,000 people had gathered together to demonstrate peacefully on the day of the Sikh New Year. Suddenly, soldiers of the British Army appeared, under the command of General Reginald Dyer. He gave the order to shoot, and for ten minutes the soldiers fired into the crowd, who were trapped in a square. Nearly 400 men, women and children were killed, and 11,000 wounded. Gandhi was horrified by the brutality of the British Army, directed at unarmed subjects of the Empire. His loyalty to the British was completely shattered. He felt they had clearly lost all right to govern.

In 1920, Gandhi became president of the All-India Home Rule League, which sought independence from the Empire. Following this, he became the leader of the Indian National Congress. He launched a massive program of non-cooperation against the British. Cotton cloth made in Britain was boycotted and clothes made of foreign material were burned on great bonfires. To symbolize getting rid of foreign influences, hand-spinning and weaving were revived throughout

Gandhi himself enjoyed spinning every day.

the country. To Gandhi, spinning represented economic progress, national unity and independence from the Empire. He himself spun daily.

HIGH IDEALS

The Indian National Congress, led by Gandhi, now called on all Indian soldiers and civilians to quit British Government service. By 1922, 30,000 people, including nearly all the Congress leaders, had been imprisoned for acts of civil disobedience. Then twenty-two policemen who had attacked the stragglers of a protest march were viciously slaughtered. Realizing that even now the nonviolent nature of *satyagraha* was not understood, Gandhi called off the campaign, and fasted again, punishing himself for the violence he felt was his fault. He was then put on trial, accused of stirring up trouble.

In court, Gandhi spoke movingly of the people's misery under British rule and of the absurd laws. He said that perhaps in reality he was innocent, but under these laws, he was guilty, so he expected the highest penalty. The judge, although he praised Gandhi "as a man of high ideals and a noble and even saintly life," sentenced him to six years' imprisonment.

Two years later, Gandhi was released. For three weeks, he fasted in protest against the increasing conflict between Hindus and Muslims. Then he turned his attention to social reforms, touring the country by train, cart, and on foot, speaking to vast crowds. Many of his followers considered him a saint, and he was showered with gifts, which he turned into funds for the cause. He taught the importance of equality for women and for people of different classes and religions. He encouraged spinning and discouraged taking alcohol or using drugs.

In 1928, a Royal Commission arrived from Britain to review the situation in India. Since it included no Indian members, it was met by protest meetings, which were broken up by the British authorities. The new proposals would have still left the country subject to British control. Now the Indian National Congress decided it could accept nothing less than complete independence.

A PINCH OF SALT

The Salt March of 1930 began a new round of nonviolent protest. Gandhi walked 322 km (200 miles) to the coast at Dandi. Thousands joined the march, watched by the world's press. On the beach after morning prayers, Gandhi picked up a lump of sea salt.

Salt was taxed; legally, only the Government could extract it from sea water. Gandhi's signal prompted people all along the coast of India to defy the law by manufacturing salt. In cities and villages, illegal salt was distributed. Following this action, about 100,000 people, including Gandhi and other Congress leaders, were imprisoned. Bravely, without violence, they faced police brutality. Many were badly beaten and some died; but eventually, the campaign succeeded, and salt manufacturing was allowed.

Later, Gandhi took part in The Round Table conference in Britain about the future of India. While in London, he chose to stay in an East End hostel for the poor. He visited Lancashire and made friends among the mill workers, even though many were unemployed because of the Indians' boycott of British cloth. He met politicians and celebrities, and went to tea at Buckingham Palace. Everywhere, he impressed

Gandhi discussed India's future at The Round Table
conference in London.
AP/Wide World

Gandhi arrives at Buckingham Palace.

people with his sincerity and humor. As for his manner of dress at the Palace, he said, "The King was wearing enough for both of us!"

Only a week later, when he returned to India, he was imprisoned again. Before long, 30,000 others had been arrested too. In prison, Gandhi carried out a prolonged fast against the class divisions among Hindus. He was willing to starve himself to death, if the barriers were not broken down throughout the country. People valued Gandhi's life so greatly that he succeeded in changing traditions that were thousands of years old. For the first time, temples were opened to *Harijans*, and all Hindus could eat together, drink water drawn from the same wells, and even marry each other.

GATHERING CLOUDS

After his release, Gandhi turned to educational and welfare work. He toured rural India, speaking on health care, village industries and reorganization, and about land ownership and justice.

Gandhi opposed Indian involvement in World War II (1939–44), believing now that all war was wholly wrong. Leading members of the Indian Congress, including his close friend Jawaharlal Nehru, disagreed. They were willing to

Gandhi and Nehru disagreed about Indian involvement in World War II.

cooperate with the British if they could obtain reforms that would lead to self-government. But Britain would give no promise of independence.

Under Gandhi's direction, people made speeches and signed written protests against taking part in the war. Thousands, including Nehru, were imprisoned for up to a year.

In 1942, Gandhi announced a new *satyagraha* campaign aimed directly at British withdrawal from India. Once again, he was imprisoned. While in prison, he fasted again, coming close to death, in protest against accusations that he had stirred up violence against the British. Kasturbai was one of 100,000 other prisoners. Her health was poor, and in 1944, she died. Feeling her loss keenly, Gandhi himself became ill, recovering only after his release a few months later. With the end of World War II, Indian independence came closer.

Gandhi had always contested religious divisions. Most Indians were either Hindus or Muslims. In the northwest and northeast of the country, Muslims were in the majority. Their leader, Muhammad Ali Jinnah, favored the creation of a separate Muslim state there, to be called Pakistan. Congress, like Gandhi, wanted a united India. Nehru was appointed Prime Minister of a provisional Indian Government, which meant

There were many scenes of violence between Muslim and Hindu groups.

Indian rule by a Hindu for that area. Jinnah announced that the Muslim League would hold a day of action to protest. The result was horrifying violence between Muslims and Hindus, with 20,000 killed or injured.

THE PEACEMAKER

From the rural area of Bengal came reports of Muslim atrocities. Gandhi walked through the villages for four months, seeking desperately to persuade people to end the violence. But soon after, in a neighboring province, there were similar Hindu atrocities to quell.

In 1947, Lord Louis Mountbatten became the last British Viceroy of India. Reluctantly, and against Gandhi's opposition, the Indian National Congress agreed that Pakistan was to become a country in its own right, separate from India. Independence came on August 15, 1947. Gandhi was living in the poorest quarters of Calcutta, where there had been appalling bloodshed, riots and fighting between the Hindu and Muslim communities. While he succeeded in pacifying the people of Bengal, the northwest was in uproar. Millions of people were migrating across the new border separating

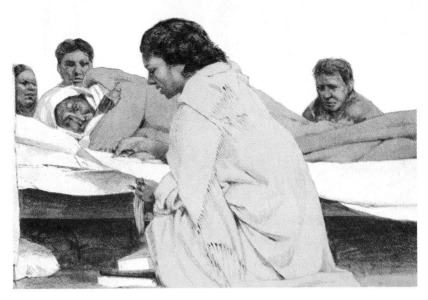

Gandhi's fast brings him near death.

"Muslim" Pakistan from "Hindu" India. Massacres were widespread, causing almost a million deaths. When violence broke out again in Calcutta, Gandhi undertook a fast "to death," refusing food until the northeast was peaceful. Then, in riot-torn Delhi, came his "greatest fast." Dramatically, it brought a pledge of peace among all the community leaders, and throughout India and Pakistan, the violence ceased.

Though millions revered him, and cherished his life so deeply, to some Hindu fanatics, Gandhi was an obstacle. On January 30, 1948, he was murdered—shot three times by an assassin who stepped from the crowd at a prayer meeting. His death caused worldwide shock and sorrow. To countless people, he was a modern-day saint, a teacher of humanity such as the world has rarely seen. As a champion of peace, his influence still remains.

A familiar image
of Mahatma Gandhi.

SWEEPING PITTSBURGH CLEAN

from MAKING HEADLINES: A BIOGRAPHY OF NELLIE BLY
by Kathy Lynn Emerson

What Elizabeth Cochrane really wanted to do was write. A female writer was not a new idea in 1885; Louisa May Alcott had been earning a living as a novelist for nearly twenty years. Elizabeth had probably read *Little Women*. If she did, she knew that Alcott's character, Jo March, stormed a newspaper office to sell her stories.

Elizabeth may have heard tales of women who were newspaper reporters, too. By 1880, almost every major newspaper in the United States paid women to write feature articles, usually essays in letter form, and send them in through the mail. In New York City, a female writer who used the name Jenny June worked in a newspaper office on a day-to-day basis. Another young woman named Sally Joy had talked herself into a job on the Boston *Post* when she was eighteen. Still, compared to New York, Pittsburgh was a small place, and its people had old-fashioned ideas. Elizabeth might never have become a journalist if it hadn't been for a newspaper column titled "What Girls Are Good For."

Elizabeth Cochrane (Nellie Bly) as a young newspaperwoman.

This essay expressed ideas held by most men in the 1880s. The writer protested the alarming trend of hiring women to work in shops and offices, and called the employment of women in business a threat to the national welfare.

Other unfair, harshly critical remarks filled the column, too. When Elizabeth Cochrane read them, she became so angry that she sat down and wrote a letter to George A. Madden, managing editor of the Pittsburgh *Dispatch*. She didn't use her name in the letter—that wouldn't have been ladylike. Instead, she signed it "Lonely Orphan Girl" and sent it off.

George Madden was so impressed by the letter that he wanted to find the author and hire him to work on the *Dispatch*. It never entered his mind that the writer might be a woman. He pictured the writer as a young man who wanted to work for the *Dispatch*, and had deliberately taken the wrong side of the issue to get attention.

On January 17, 1885, an advertisement appeared in the *Dispatch*, asking "Lonely Orphan Girl" to contact Mr. Madden. Once more Elizabeth addressed a note to the editor, but this time she signed her own name. Mr. Madden may have groaned in dismay, imagining some old "battle-ax" with strong feminist views, but he wrote back anyway. She did, after all, write well. He said that he would be willing to consider publishing an article on "girls and their spheres in life" in the Sunday paper if she would write and submit it.

Elizabeth sent in the article as soon as she could get it written, and Madden liked it. He paid her five dollars, and published her work on January 25 under the title "The Girl Puzzle." Then, throwing caution to the wind, Madden wrote to Elizabeth once more to ask if she had any other suggestions for stories. He had no idea how she would respond, but the last thing he expected was that she would turn up several days later at the Fifth Street offices of the *Dispatch*.

Elizabeth Cochrane appeared fragile for her height of five feet five inches. She wore her chestnut-colored hair in a chignon with bangs, a youthful style in those days, and had a jaunty sailor hat on her head. In spite of the determined gleam in her wide hazel eyes, she had a meek and mild appearance. The *Dispatch's* reporters, who shared the one big city room, didn't know what to think of her.

Newspaper offices in the nineteenth century echoed with the clatter of presses from the floors below. The rooms smelled of printer's ink, gaslights, and tobacco, and were filled with a haze of cigar smoke. Chewing tobacco was popular, too, and the men were often careless when they aimed at the spittoons. The floors were filthy. In Sally Joy's city room in Boston, the more gentlemanly reporters put newspapers down so she wouldn't get her long skirts stained with tobacco juice.

In the nineteenth century, newspaper offices such as this one were not considered proper places for a young lady to work.

Elizabeth Cochrane looked out of place in this setting. A more timid woman would have turned and fled, but her lady-like appearance masked a will of iron. She informed the gawking reporters, sitting at desks crowded together and piled high with copy paper, that Mr. Madden had sent for her. When they directed her to his desk, she introduced herself and said she had come with her ideas.

If George Madden was surprised by Elizabeth Cochrane's sudden appearance in his city room, he was shocked by the subject on which she wanted to write. Divorce, she told him, was an issue that needed to be discussed in the newspaper.

Elizabeth tried hard to persuade Mr. Madden to give her a chance. He protested at first, but finally agreed to let her prove she could do what she said she could. He sent her home to write her article on divorce, and probably thought he would never see her again.

Elizabeth, however, tackled her new project immediately. She had the notes on divorce cases that her father had made during his years as a judge, but she had been doing some research of her own as well. Since she and her mother had spent almost all of their inheritance from her father, they had changed addresses several times, each time selecting a less expensive place. By the time "What Girls Are Good For" was printed, they were living in rundown lodgings in a poor section of the city, where Elizabeth had talked to several women who had suffered because of unfair divorce laws.

All night long, Elizabeth worked on her article, writing and revising, scratching out passages and copying it over. At that time there were no word processors and no portable typewriters to make the work easier. Even in the newspaper offices, articles were composed with pen and ink. Despite the long, slow process, Elizabeth persisted until her story was just the way she wanted it. The next morning she returned to the *Dispatch* office with a final draft that was neat and easy to read. More importantly, the article said something. Mr. Madden was impressed and immediately agreed to publish the story.

George Madden was a businessman. He might have believed, as the article in his paper had said, that respectable women stayed at home until they married, or at worst went into a "woman's profession" such as teaching or nursing. Still, he knew the facts. Since the Civil War, women had been working in mills, factories, and offices. The thought of a woman in politics made him shudder, but a woman had run for president in 1884.

In spite of his doubts, Madden found himself encouraging Elizabeth Cochrane. If one thing could overcome his prejudices, it was the promise of a controversial series for his newspaper. Controversy increased a newspaper's circulation, and that was good business.

He asked for more stories, saying that if the series on divorce were a success, he would give Elizabeth a regular job and pay her five dollars a week. She accepted at once.

Madden had only one problem left. He was worried about allowing Elizabeth to use her own name. What would people say if they knew he had hired an eighteen-year-old girl to write on such a sensitive subject as divorce? What would her family say? She had respectable and old-fashioned older brothers who would not approve of her new career.

Just as Mr. Madden and Elizabeth Cochrane agreed to invent a pen name, Mr. Madden's assistant, Erasmus Wilson, began to hum a popular Stephen Foster song. Everyone knew the words:

> Nelly Bly, Nelly Bly,
> bring the broom along.
> We'll sweep the kitchen clear, my dear,
> and have a little song.
> Poke the wood, my lady love,
> and make the fire burn,
> And while I take the banjo down,
> just give the mush a turn.
> Heigh, Nelly, Ho, Nelly,
> listen love, to me;
> I'll sing for you, play for you,
> a dulcet melody.

From that day on, Elizabeth Cochrane was Nellie Bly, and Madden immediately published her articles on divorce. The subject alone was enough to make people sit up and take notice, but the newspaper-reading public of Pittsburgh was just as intrigued by the author. Who was this Nellie Bly? they wondered.

The *Dispatch* made the most of the mystery surrounding its new reporter's identity. Circulation improved dramatically as Nellie wrote more articles. In time, she came up with an idea that would set the tone for her entire newspaper career—she asked Mr. Madden if she could write about life in the slums and factories of Pittsburgh. As a reporter and a reformer, she would tell the real story of her own experiences visiting these places, from a lady's point of view. She would take an artist with her to sketch what she saw. Mr. Madden

An aerial view of Pittsburgh in the late nineteenth century.

Historical Society of Western Pennsylvania

saw the circulation of the *Dispatch* going up and up . . . and agreed.

Nellie brought the broom along, as the song says, and set out to sweep Pittsburgh clean. It needed it. Under smoke-blackened skies, which glowed flame red at night, workers were little more than slaves to uncaring factory owners. Women in a bottle factory worked fourteen-hour days in an unheated building. Children were endangered by living in dirty, disease-ridden, fire-prone buildings in a slum called the Point.

When Nellie Bly joined the staff of the *Dispatch*, more than 156,000 people lived in Pittsburgh. Many were immigrants, drawn by jobs in the iron and steel industries. Few labor unions protected these unskilled workers, and no social service agencies existed.

Nellie brought her discoveries of social injustices to public attention through the *Dispatch*. She was not content to sit at her hard-won desk in the city room, letting others do the research. Every story was her own, from the first idea, through

the investigation and writing, to her byline, or name, on the
finished article.

A bottling factory was Nellie's first target. The glass indus-
try was Pittsburgh's third largest business; some seventy factories produced half the nation's glass, and more champagne
bottles than there were in France. Accompanied by her artist,
she located the factory owner and told him she wanted to
write an article for the *Dispatch* about his factory. Deceived by
her ladylike manner and pleasant smile, he welcomed her
with open arms. He thought she was offering him good, free
publicity, so he told her to talk to anyone and look anywhere.

Nellie talked to the workers as the artist sketched. Some of
these women stood on an icy cement floor for fourteen hours
at a stretch. To cope with the winter cold that seeped through
the factory walls, the workers had to wrap rags around their

Women working in a Pittsburgh bottling factory in the early 1890s.

feet, which kept their toes from freezing. Several hundred workers shared one toilet, along with a family of rats. Worse yet was the daily risk of injury from broken or exploding bottles. Since worker's compensation did not exist, an injury could result in the loss of a person's job and only source of income.

Nellie was shocked by the conditions in the factories, and she channeled all her outrage into print. She held nothing back, including names, dates, and drawings. When her article appeared in the *Dispatch*, every copy of that day's paper sold quickly at the city's newsstands.

The factory owners were enraged when they saw Nellie's articles. Letters flooded the *Dispatch* office. Although Nellie faced protests, and even threats, efforts at reform began which eventually improved conditions in the factories of Pittsburgh.

Nellie attacked the slums next. In the course of her own frequent moves, she had seen how crowded many of the city's tenement buildings were. In the Point she found a family of

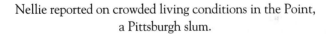
Nellie reported on crowded living conditions in the Point,
a Pittsburgh slum.

The run-down tenement houses of Pittsburgh's Yellow Row
were another of Nellie's targets.

twelve living in one unheated room. In the rickety wooden shanties along Yellow Row, and the ramshackle cottages on the hill at Skunk Hollow, Nellie Bly asked questions and got answers. When she wrote her story, she named the slumlords, hoping to shame them into repairing their buildings.

The uproar this time was even greater than it had been after her article about the factory. Pittsburgh businessmen began to organize against the threat of Nellie Bly. They claimed she was ruining the city's reputation. Despite fourteen thousand chimneys that polluted the air, they still insisted that Pittsburgh was one of the healthiest cities in the United States. In fact, they said that people worked so hard that they didn't notice the smoke. Pollution had killed the grass and flowers, but a child who complained about the foulness of the air was told she should be "grateful for God's goodness in making work, which made smoke, which made prosperity." With that kind of thinking, no wonder the businessmen threatened George Madden with the loss of all his advertising if he didn't stop those reform-minded articles by Nellie Bly.

George Madden's business sense told him it was time to let things cool down. He gave Nellie a raise to ten dollars a week and made her society editor for the *Dispatch*. Nellie Bly began writing about the upper classes, whose parties, art, drama, and books were part of a world far removed from the city's slums.

Plays, lectures, concerts, and charity balls soon left Nellie bored and restless. "I was too impatient," she wrote, "to work along at the usual duties assigned women on newspapers." Yet nearly a year passed before she could persuade Mr. Madden to let her write serious articles again.

A modern jail, Riverside Penitentiary of Western Pennsylvania, had just been built to replace the old Western Penitentiary. It was the most up-to-date facility of its kind, and Nellie wanted to visit it. Her article would be full of praise, she argued. Why not let her cover its opening? Reluctantly, Madden agreed.

In her article, Nellie praised the new facility's separate cells for inmates and large common work and recreation areas, but she used this praise of one jail as a starting point to criticize the rest. When Madden read her attack on other Pennsylvania jails, he knew trouble lay ahead, but he decided to print the article anyway.

Meanwhile, Nellie wanted to take another look at the factories. This time she went undercover, dressing herself as a poor woman looking for a job. She was hired at the first factory where she applied, though she had no skills. Her job was to hitch cables together in an assembly line with other young women. They could be fined for talking, or even for smiling, but Nellie did manage to learn that they all suffered from headaches.

She soon understood why. The light was so dim that her head began to ache, too. Then her feet started to hurt, because she had to stand. Her hands became raw and started to bleed. Before long, she ached all over. Just like the workers in the bottle factory, these young women kept working in spite of their fear of blindness and the constant discomfort. They had to work to live.

The women's supervisor kept urging them to work faster and faster. He paced back and forth behind them, yelling out threats and foul language. Since Nellie had been brought up to have good manners, she found it difficult to listen to curses and insults for hours on end. Finally, Nellie simply walked away from the assembly line to get a drink of water. The foreman fired her.

When Nellie's two stories appeared in the *Dispatch*, the response was overwhelming. The paper's sales increased, and Nellie was criticized by just about everyone. City law enforcement officials said she wasn't qualified to judge their jails. The clergy called her shameless for visiting a men's prison without a chaperon. Again, the factory owners and businessmen of Pittsburgh threatened to withdraw their advertising. Madden raised Nellie's pay to fifteen dollars a week and sent her back to write the society page.

The other reporters of the *Dispatch* appreciated her, even if the targets of her articles didn't. "Only a few months previous I had become a newspaper woman," she wrote, and in October 1886, she became the first woman invited to join the Pittsburgh Press Club.

THE PUTSCH THAT FAILED

Harrison Rainie with Douglas Pasternak and Douglas Stanglin

*In March of 1985, Mikhail Sergeyevich Gorbachev
became general secretary of the Communist Party and chief
political leader of the Soviet Union. In 1990, he also became
president of the Soviet Union.*

*Shortly after assuming power in 1985, Gorbachev introduced
a program of economic and social reforms that began shifting
power away from the totalitarian central government and
allowing the Soviet citizens greater individual liberties. His policies
of glasnost (openness) and perestroika (restructuring) expanded
the powers and freedom of the media, allowed for multicandidate
political contests and elections by secret ballot, introduced limited
free-market economic practices and private ownership of some
businesses, and encouraged the creation of citizens' groups.
Slowly, totalitarian rule was being abolished.*

*Communist Party officials and leaders of the central
government bureaucracy who saw their power and authority
being taken from them resisted Gorbachev's democratic reforms.
In August of 1991, a handful of men representing the opposition
attempted to seize the government from Gorbachev.*

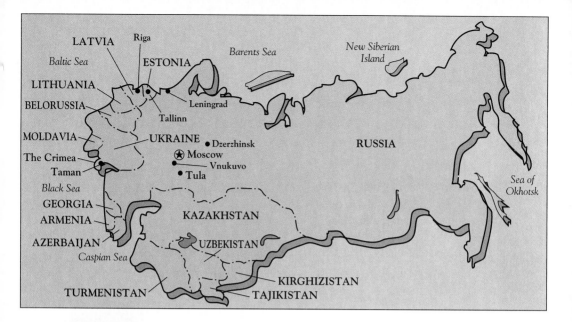

LATVIA Riga
Baltic Sea ESTONIA
Barents Sea
New Siberian
Island
LITHUANIA
BELORUSSIA
Leningrad
Tallinn
MOLDAVIA UKRAINE • Dzerzhinsk
The Crimea ⊛ Moscow
Taman Vnukuvo
Black Sea • Tula
GEORGIA
ARMENIA KAZAKHSTAN
AZERBAIJAN UZBEKISTAN
Caspian Sea
RUSSIA
Sea of
Okhotsk
KIRGHIZISTAN
TURMENISTAN TAJIKISTAN

SUNDAY AUGUST 18

An unanticipated visit. Like the countless millions grabbed for the Soviet gulag, Mikhail Gorbachev learned of his date with totalitarian security after an unexpected knock on the door. At 4:50 P.M., aides told the Soviet president that they had allowed a mysterious group led by Yuri Plekhanov, a powerful KGB official, into Gorbachev's Crimean *dacha*. Dumbfounded, Gorbachev quickly tried each of the government phones in his office, discovering all were dead. What he later called his personal "drama" had begun.

Fearing he might be assassinated, Gorbachev went to his family's quarters, gathering his wife, Raisa, his daughter, Irina, and son-in-law, Anatoly, to break the news. "If the worst happens, if it's a question of [giving up my] political course, I will stand up for my position," he said. They agreed it was the only option, even if it put their own lives at risk.

Gorbachev left to confront his captors, but before he could usher them in, they had entered on their own. To his shock, their leader was his own chief of staff, Valery Boldin. Gorbachev first tried bluster: "Who sent you?" "The emergency committee," came the response. "I didn't appoint such a committee," he stormed. They pressed their ultimatum: He must either sign a decree authorizing an emergency crackdown to undo much of the reform he had championed in the past six years, or turn over his power to an emergency group led by his handpicked vice president, Gennadi Yanayev. Gorbachev refused, vowing silently to commit suicide rather than accede: "Those who sent you are reckless adventurers. You're going to kill yourselves."

The arrest interrupted Gorbachev while he was drafting a speech he planned to give two days later at the signing of a new union treaty transferring unprecedented powers from the central Soviet government to the increasingly active republics. "I was totally isolated from the sea and from the land," Gorbachev related later. "Everything was done to weaken me

Gorbachev recorded a videotape to prove he was in good health.
AP/Wide World

psychologically." But his 32-man guard remained with him, providing what protection they could for his family. With an eye to his own death and place in history, Gorbachev recorded a videotape to prove he was in good health and resisting the coup. He passed it piece by piece to his guards when they brought food, in the hope it would be spliced together if he were killed. He also wrote a will.

Another cause for alarm: His captors seized the briefcase that contained his codes to launch nuclear weapons, raising the prospect that, in desperation, the coup leaders might attempt nuclear blackmail.

MONDAY AUGUST 19 **The tanks roll.** Gorbachev's refusal to comply with the conspirators' script set off the slipshod machinery of the coup. At 2 A.M., the KGB went on alert around the sprawling country. Hours later, thousands of Soviet soldiers with their armored vehicles were ordered to prepare to head for Moscow. Air defense forces parked tractors on a runway near Gorbachev's *dacha* to keep his Tu-134 airliner and helicopter from leaving. Several KGB units sealed off the area around the home, helicopters circled overhead and more than a half-dozen patrol boats monitored the coast.

But the coup planners sealed their fate in these first hours by failing to decapitate their opposition. The KGB missed arresting Russian Republic President Boris Yeltsin at his home because he had rushed off to the Russian parliament 45 minutes earlier—his first anticoup appeal to the nation already in hand—after receiving an intercepted radio communication. In fact, none of the opposition leaders in any republic was arrested.

By the time the plotters' tanks reached Red Square,
Yeltsin was in position at the Russian parliament.
© Klaus Reisinger/Black Star

At 6:29 A.M. in Moscow, the plotters went public. The Soviet news agency Tass announced that Yanayev had taken over because Gorbachev was suffering "health" problems. But the real powers behind the curtain had names like Pugo (Boris K., interior minister); Kryuchkov (Vladimir A., chairman of the KGB); Yazov (Dmitri T., defense minister) and Pavlov (Valentin S., prime minister). Even before they filled the streets with tanks, they showed their Stalinist colors by

The press conference staged by the coup leaders that afternoon
showed them to be indecisive.
© Klaus Reisinger/Black Star

issuing a resolution declaring all media organs under official control and banning all strikes and demonstrations.

The takeover was neither peaceful nor orderly. At 9:47 A.M., the Soviet Army rumbled into Moscow to the cries of *"Pozor!"*—shame!—from distraught onlookers. Fifteen minutes later, Soviet troops surrounded the transmission tower of Lithuania's government. An hour after that, tanks surrounded the parliament of the Russian Republic. Soviet troops invaded TV stations in Riga, the Latvian capital, to seize control of the main television station. They also killed a bus driver and wounded one passenger.

Rather than wither away, the resistance mounted a tit-for-tat counter-strategy. When Yeltsin learned of Yanayev's role, he phoned the new national boss with a challenge: "Keep in mind that we do not accept you gang of bandits." Brushing aside aides' admonitions that he was overplaying his weak hand, Yeltsin climbed atop one of the Soviet tanks on the

A defiant Yeltsin climbed aboard a tank on the first full day of the crisis to urge fellow citizens to resist.

© Bagayev/A.F.P. Photo

streets outside his office to ask the crowd of 20,000 to participate in massive resistance and a general strike the following day. As an inspirational spectacle, it was electric.

That afternoon, Yeltsin's office issued the first of a blizzard of decrees, ordering, among other things, that KGB officers obey *his* commands in Russia, not those of their national masters. Meanwhile, groups of young Afghan War veterans began appearing at the parliament building, offering help in erecting barricades and making Molotov cocktails.

On the defensive, the leaders of the coup called a press conference to argue their right to remove the man who had presided over a 25 percent collapse in the Soviet GNP (Gross National Product). "The situation has gone out of control," Yanayev charged. "We're also facing a threat of disintegration." But it was clear Gorbachev's betrayers had no strategy to fix the problem.

A harbinger of the plotters' downfall came toward the end of the first day. Shortly before midnight, 10 tanks from the

Overturned trolleys formed part of the barricades erected
against the putsch's armor.

© Klaus Reisinger/Black Star

elite Soviet Taman Motorized Rifle Division maneuvered in front of the Russian parliament building, known as the White House, until their cannons were in position to defend Yeltsin against the rest of the Soviet Army.

TUESDAY AUGUST 20

Putsch comes to shove. Inside the Yeltsin bunker, the sleepless resisters knew their fate would depend on whether the public turned out in the streets the next day. They were not disappointed. In Moscow, Leningrad and several other cities hundreds of thousands chanted "Yeltsin!" "Yeltsin!" The emboldened Russian responded with new demands: the right to meet with Gorbachev within 24 hours; the dropping of restrictions on the media; the lifting of the state of emergency; the return of troops to their bases and the arrest of coup leaders. Fence-sitters and even early agents of betrayal began to cross the line. The commander of the Tula airborne division refused his allegiance and directed his men to protect the Russian parliament. The chief of Leningrad's police and the local Leningrad KGB chief said they, too, supported Yeltsin.

Yet inside the Moscow White House, there was fear. KGB agents who turned up at the door claiming a change of heart and volunteering help were closely questioned to test their sincerity. "I don't have much time left," Yeltsin told an anguished John Major, Britain's prime minister, during a phone call. Pistols were passed out to Yeltsin aides, and boxes of Molotov cocktails were strategically placed. To resist attack, military deserters manned makeshift communications lines, taking in intelligence reports of troop movements and other developments.

The emergency committee ordered an 11 P.M.-to-5 A.M. curfew in Moscow, banned all but its own radio and TV broadcasts and ordered Yeltsin's allies to clear their barricades. But their demonstrations of power were all for show. In Estonia, more than 100 Soviet armored vehicles and trucks rolled into the capital, Tallinn, but did not disrupt the media or communication with the outside world. In Moscow, the tanks still loyal to the hard-liners just raced up and down the street in front of the White House as if caught in some hellish traffic circle.

The "health problems" afflicting Gorbachev suddenly appeared to be catching among the coup leaders. Pavlov was reported hospitalized with high blood pressure; two of his colleagues were also rumored to be ill. The KGB's Kryuchkov raised his head, opening conciliatory discussions with Yeltsin during the afternoon and then promising that the military would not storm the White House. There was no assurance that he was telling the truth.

The most anxious moments came that evening, when Yeltsin's camp was tipped that a tank attack was imminent. All women were ordered out of the building, lights were doused to protect against snipers spotted in nearby buildings and orders were given to shoot anyone who stepped within a 50-meter no-man's land around the White House. Overhead, Yeltsin's followers had lofted a dirigible draped in the Russian flag, in the hope that it would help deter incoming helicopters. Inside, the world's pre-eminent cellist, Mstislav Rostropovich, who had flown in from Paris to show solidarity with the protesters, played soaring music in the darkened parliament.

Deliverance. The nightmare outcome appeared to unfold at 1:30 A.M. when Soviet tanks from the Dzerzhinksy and Taman divisions became entangled in the human chain around Yeltsin's White House and protesters swarmed over the first tank. A second tank tried to maneuver around and was pelted with Molotov cocktails. A brawl broke out and two Yeltsin supporters were shot and one crushed by an armored vehicle. But the tanks withdrew. The democrats had held.

Moscow's youth gave the retreating tanks
a high-spirited escort.

© Klaus Reisinger/Black Star

So desperate were the coup schemers that the next morning KGB boss Kryuchkov suggested that Yeltsin travel to Gorbachev's home to see his condition. "Of course I refused," Yeltsin later reported. Less than an hour after Kryuchkov's offer, Yeltsin returned to the parliament podium to tell stomping, cheering delegates that the Gang of Eight was trying to flee Moscow. Russian police forces just missed catching them en route to Vnukovo Airport several miles outside the city. Yazov and Kryuchkov flew to the Crimea, apparently to seek a pardon from Gorbachev. In his *dacha*, Gorbachev refused to meet with them and demanded a phone. His first call was to his savior, Yeltsin. Shortly afterwards, a second plane from Moscow arrived, carrying a Yeltsin delegation led by officials of the Russian republic. Yazov and Kryuchkov were put in custody for the return trip to Moscow. Four others would soon be arrested and a fifth was being sought for questioning. The interior minister, Pugo, killed himself with a bullet in the head; his wife was found critically injured by his side. In Moscow, a huge traffic jam ensued as a 3-mile-long convoy of tanks and other vehicles made its way back to nearby bases.

Gorbachev returned in the next day's dawn to confront the depths of the treachery against him by men he had "believed in." Even his friend and college classmate, Anatoly Lukyanov, chairman of the Soviet parliament, appeared to have dirty hands as Yeltsin supporters fingered him as the ideological mastermind of the coup. As Gorbachev's countrymen stomped on the symbols of their oppression, the woebegone leader began a purge of his revealed enemies and then purged himself by resigning as general secretary of the Communist Party.

Citizens became so emboldened that they dared topple a statue of Felix Dzerzhinsky, the KGB's founder.

© A. Sapronenkov/A.F.P. Photo

Gorbachev returns from his ordeal.

AP/Wide World

BIBLIOGRAPHY

Ain't Gonna Study War No More by Milton Meltzer. Meltzer's book is about pacifism and the brave men and women who have raised their voices against war and violence.

Cesar Chavez by Consuelo Rodriguez. This is the biography of the Mexican-American labor activist who organized migrant farm workers in their bitter struggle for better wages and working conditions.

Grandpa's Mountain by Carolyn Reeder. The government wants to turn the land around Virginia's Blue Ridge Mountains into a national park. Find out what happens when Carrie's Grandpa refuses to be evicted from his beloved mountain home.

Jayhawker by Patricia Beatty. Lije Tulley, a young abolitionist and Union spy during the Civil War, infiltrates a ruthless gang of Confederates.

A Long Hard Journey: The Story of the Pullman Porter by Patricia and Fredrick McKissack. After years of abuse at the hands of the Pullman Car Company, A. Philip Randolph formed America's first legitimate African-American labor union.

Matt's Crusade by Margot Marek. Is joining an anti-nuclear missile protest worth the possibility of angering his family, getting kicked off the football team, or getting arrested? Matt Tyson must decide.

Number the Stars by Lois Lowry. Annemarie Johansen and her family harbor a young Jewish girl in Denmark during World War II.

Robin Hood by Paul Creswick. Robin Hood and his band of Merry Men settle in Sherwood Forest where they defy the Sheriff of Nottingham's unjust laws and high taxes.

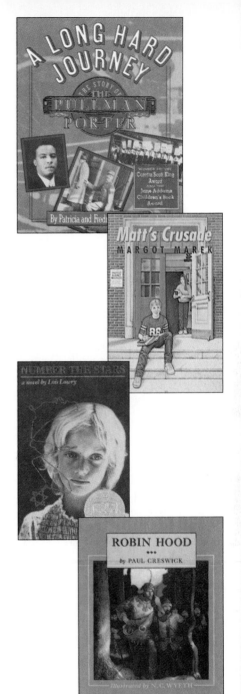

GLOSSARY

ablution (ə blo͞oʹ shən) *n.* A
cleansing.

abolition (abʹ ə lishʹ ən) *n.* The
termination, or ending, of
something.

abolitionist (abʹ ə lishʹ ən ist) *n.* A
person who wanted to end
slavery.

accede (ak sēdʹ) *v.* To agree.

accursed (ə kûrʹ sid) *adj.* Affected
by a curse or a spell.

acrylic (ə krilʹ ik) *n.* A synthetic,
or human-made, liquid that dries
clear and hard like plastic.

adobe (ə dōʹ bē) *n.* Sun-dried
brick.

aggravate (agʹ rə vātʹ) *v.* To annoy.

alkali (alʹ kə līʹ) *n.* A chemical
compound or element that forms
salts and neutralizes acids.

ambassador (am basʹ ə dər) *n.* A
representative; one who
represents something.

amethyst (amʹ ə thist) *n.* A purple
or violet gem.

amphitheater (amʹ fə thēʹ ə tər) *n.*
An area with flat ground
surrounded by rising hills or cliffs.

amply (amʹ plē) *adv.* Sufficiently;
plentifully; enough.

366

anoint (ə noint´) *v.* To apply oil or ointment as part of a religious ceremony; to make sacred in a ceremony.

anthropologist (an´ thrə pol´ ə jist) *n.* A scientist who studies the various physical aspects or cultural features of human beings.

antislavery (an´ tē slā´ və rē) *adj.* Against slavery.

aria (är´ ē ə) *n.* A song that is sung by one person in an opera.

aristocracy (ar´ ə stok´ rə sē) *n.* The upper class.

aristocrat (ə ris´ tə krat´) *n.* An upper-class person.

arroyo (ə roi´ ō) *n.* A small gulch or gulley.

asinine (as´ ə nīn´) *adj.* Silly; stupid.

astuteness (ə sto͞ot´ nəs) *n.* Cleverness; shrewdness.

attain (ə tān´) *v.* To reach; to gain; to accomplish.

audacious (ô dā´ shəs) *adj.* Extremely daring; recklessly brave.

augment (ôg ment´) *v.* To add to; to increase; to enlarge.

aura (or´ ə) *n.* A certain quality; an atmosphere surrounding something.

authorize (ô´ thə rīz´) *v.* To make legal; to give legal power to.

Autoharp (ô´ tō härp´) *n.* A small instrument that is strummed; a zither.

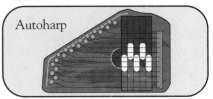
Autoharp

awl (ôl) *n.* A pointed tool for poking holes in things.

balustrade (bal´ ə strād´) *n.* A railing with upright supports.

barge (bärj) *n.* A flat-bottomed boat used for carrying freight.

bastings (bā´ stingz) *n.* Long, loose stitches that are usually removed when final stitches are put in.

belabor (bi lā´ bər) *v.* To beat; to hit.

biceps (bī´ seps) *n.* A muscle in the upper arm.

blackguard (blag´ ärd) *n.* A scoundrel; a bad person.

boogie-woogie (bo͞og´ ē wo͞og´ ē) *n.* A type of jazz played on the piano.

boycott (boi´ kot) *v.* To refuse to do business with someone.

bridal garland (brīd′ l gär′ lənd) *n.* A wreath of flowers for a wedding ceremony.

bull-roarer (bŏŏl′ ror′ ər) *n.* A strip of wood on a string that is twirled around one's head to make a roaring sound.

burg (bûrg) *n.* A small town.

calypso (kə lip′ sō) *n.* A style of jazz from the West Indies.

cellist (chel′ ist) *n.* A musician who plays the cello, a large stringed instrument.

chamber (chām′ bər) *n.* 1. A room in a royal palace, especially a bedroom. 2. An enclosed space.

chamberlain (chām′ bər lin) *n.* An important official in a royal court.

chaperon (shap′ ə rōn′) *n.* A person who stays with a young, unmarried woman in public.

chaplain (chap′ lin) *n.* A religious leader in a royal court.

chaunt (chônt) *v. obsolete.* To chant.

chignon (shēn′ yon) *n.* A twist or knot of hair worn at the nape of the neck.

cicada (si kā′ də) *n.* A large insect that makes a shrill sound.

circulation (sûr′ kyə lā′ shən) *n.* The number of newspapers sold to readers.

cite (sīt) *v.* To state as proof or as an example.

civil disobedience (siv′ əl dis′ ə bē′ dē əns) *n.* The refusal to obey certain laws in order to eventually change those laws.

civilization (siv′ ə lə zā′ shən) *n.* A culture, society, or group of human beings who have developed education, agriculture, trade, science, art, government, and so on.

cog (kog) *n.* The part of a gear that sticks out like a tooth; a tiny part of a machine.

cog

concept (kon′ sept) *n.* An idea.

conciliatory (kən sil′ ē ə tor′ ē) *adj.* Peaceful; coming together in agreement.

condescending (kon´ də sen´ ding) *adj.* Acting as if one is coming down to the level of a person thought of as inferior.

conservatory (kən sûr´ və tor´ ē) *n.* A school where music is studied.

constitutional amendment (kon´ sti tōō´ shə nl ə mend´ mənt) *n.* A change added to the Constitution of the United States.

contagious (kən tā´ jəs) *adj.* Spreading by touch or by contact.

contempt (kən tempt´) *n.* Scorn; disdain.

contest (kən test´) *v.* To struggle against.

controversy (kon´ trə vûr´ sē) *n.* Disagreement; strife.

coquetry (kō´ ki trē) *n.* Flirting.

coup (kōō) *n.* 1. A daring deed in battle, especially touching an enemy without being harmed. 2. The overthrow of a government.

courtier (kor´ tē ər) *n.* A person in attendance at a royal court.

cradleboard (krād´ l bord´) *n.* A wooden frame that Native American women wore on their backs to carry their babies.

crayfish (krā´ fish´) *n.* A freshwater shellfish like a small lobster.

creditor (kred´ i tər) *n.* One to whom money is owed.

creed (krēd) *n.* A statement of belief.

cremate (krē´ māt) *v.* To burn to ashes.

crescent (kres´ ənt) *n.* A curved shape like a new moon.

croon (krōōn) *v.* To sing in a low, moaning tone.

culmination (kul´ mə nā´ shən) *n.* The end; the finish.

curious (kyōōr´ ē əs) *adj.*
1. Strange. 2. Interesting.
3. Prying; inquisitive; wanting to know.

curtail (kər tāl´) *v.* To cut short; to put a stop to.

curvaceous (kûr vā´ shəs) *adj.* Having curves.

dacha (dä´ chə) *n.* A Russian country house.

dank (dangk) *adj.* Damp; moist.

decapitate (di kap´ i tāt´) *v.* To cut the head off something.

deign (dān) *v.* To lower oneself.

delirium (di lēr´ ē əm) *n.* A state of excitability; a madness.

deluded (di lōō´ did) *adj.* Misled; deceived.

deport (di port´) *v.* To banish; to
expel from a country.

depression (di presh´ ən) *n.* A
shallow hole or a dent.

despise (di spīz´) *v.* To look down
on; to scorn.

deter (di tûr´) *v.* To hold back; to
prevent.

dictate (dik´ tāt) *v.* To prescribe; to
command.

dirigible (dir´ i jə bəl) *n.* An
airship; a blimp.

disbursement (dis bûrs´ mənt) *n.*
Money spent.

discord (dis´ kord) *n.*
Disagreement.

discordant (dis kor´ dnt) *adj.*
Harsh; jarring.

disintegration (dis in´ tə grā´ shən)
n. A falling apart; a crumbling.

disparage (di spar´ ij) *v.* To belittle;
to run down.

divination (div´ ə nā´ shən) *n.* The
act of telling the future by using
magic or occult methods.

document (dok´ yə mənt) *n.* A
written proof or testimony.

dulcet (dul´ sit) *adj.* Pleasant;
soothing.

dumb (dum) *adj.* Unable to talk.

durable (dŏŏr´ ə bəl) *adj.* Lasting;
long-wearing.

ebony (eb´ ə nē) *n.* A dark, heavy
wood from Africa.

eccentric (ik sen´ trik) *adj.* Odd;
peculiar.

ecstatic (ek stat´ ik) *adj.* Extremely
joyful; intensely happy.

Elysium (i lizh´ ē əm) *n.* The place
where the good go after death,
according to ancient Greek
religious ideas.

embalmer (em bäm´ ər) *n.* A
person who preserves dead bodies.

encrusted (en krust´ id) *adj.*
Covered with.

engage (en gāj´) *v.* To employ; to
hire.

engender (en jen´ dər) *v.* To
produce; to cause.

enlightened (en līt´ nd) *adj.*
Informed; educated.

enthralled (en thrôld´) *adj.*
Charmed; fascinated.

entity (en´ ti tē) *n.* Something that
exists on its own.

entrails (en´ trālz) *n.* The organs inside the body.

entrepreneur (än´ trə prə nûr´) *n.* A person who starts a business that usually involves risk.

envision (en vizh´ ən) *v.* To see in one's mind, especially the future.

epistle (i pis´ əl) *n.* A letter; a message.

equation (i kwā´ zhən) *n.* A mathematical statement that shows how two things are equal.

esperanto (es´ pə rän´ tō) *n. usually capitalized.* A language that was invented in hopes that all the people in the world could speak the same language.

etch (ech) *v.* To produce a design by making furrows on a hard surface.

ewer (yoo´ ər) *n.* A pitcher or jug.

ewer

excavate (eks´ kə vāt´) *v.* To dig out.

exigency (ek´ si jən sē) *n.* Urgency; the need to act immediately.

exquisite (ik skwiz´ it) *adj.* Having special or rare beauty.

extent (ik stent´) *n.* The size; the amount.

fanatic (fə nat´ ik) *n.* A person who is carried beyond reason by feelings or beliefs.

fathomless (fath´ əm lis) *adj.* Extremely deep; bottomless.

feminist (fem´ ə nist) *adj.* Agreeing with equal rights for women.

fetter (fet´ ər) *n.* A chain binding the ankles.

flatiron (flat´ ī´ ərn) *n.* An iron that is not electric, used to press clothes.

fluted (floo´ tid) *adj.* Having rounded grooves.

foremost (for´ mōst´) *adj.* The most important.

frankincense (frang´ kin sens´) *n.* A substance with an aroma, burned as incense or used as perfume.

fraud (frôd) *n.* Someone who pretends to be something that he or she isn't; an imposter.

frieze (frēz) *n.* An ornamental border around the walls of a room or the outside of a building.

galley (gal´ ē) *n.* A ship's kitchen.

Pronunciation Key: at; l**ā**te; c**â**re; f**ä**ther; s**e**t; m**ē**; **it**; k**ī**te; **ox**; r**ō**se; **ô** in b**ou**ght; c**oi**n; b**oo**k; t**oo**; f**or**m; **ou**t; **up**; t**û**rn; **ə** sound in about, chicken, pencil, cannon, circus; **ch**air; **hw** in **wh**ich; ri**ng**; **sh**op; **th**in; **th**ere; **zh** in treasure.

garnet (gär´ nit) *n.* A deep red gem.

gig (gig) *n.* A short job for musicians.

glowering (glou´ ər ing) *adj.* Scowling; frowning.

GNP Gross national product: The total amount of money a country earns in one year.

gulag (goo´ läg) *n.* The forced-labor prison system of the former Soviet Union.

gunwale (gun´ l) *n.* The top edge of a boat's side.

gypsum (jip´ səm) *n.* A soft white mineral, or nonliving substance, that occurs in nature. The type of gypsum used in carvings and building is known as alabaster.

halflight (haf´ līt´) *n.* Dimmed light.

hamlet (ham´ lit) *n.* A small village.

harbinger (här´ bin jər) *n.* A forerunner; a forecaster; one who gives a clue in advance.

harpsichord (härp´ si kord´) *n.* A musical instrument like a small piano, but with a more delicate sound.

harpsichord

Hebrides (heb´ ri dēz´) *n.* A group of islands off the coast of Scotland.

henna (hen´ ə) *n.* A reddish-orange dye.

hew (hyoo) *v.* To cut with an axe.

hogan (hō´ gôn) *n.* The rounded, log and mud dwelling of the Navajo.

homage (hom´ ij) *n.* Duty; loyalty; devotion.

ibis (ī´ bis) *n.* A large wading bird with a long bill that curves downward.

immortal (i mor´ tl) *adj.* Living forever.

implore (im plor´) *v.* To beg.

impoverished (im pov´ ər isht) *adj.* Very poor.

improvise (im´ prə vīz´) *v.* To write music without planning, by just playing on an instrument.

inclined (in klīnd´) *adj.* Tending to be in favor of.

inconsolable (in´ kən sō´ lə bəl) *adj.* Not able to be comforted.

indispensable (in´ di spen´ sə bəl) *adj.* Necessary; essential.

inexistent (in´ ig zis´ tənt) *adj.* Not living; not being.

infinite (in´ fə nit) *adj.* Having no limits; endless; immense.

infuriated (in fyōōr´ ē ā´ təd) *adj.* Enraged; furious.

ingenuity (in jə nōō´ i tē) *n.* Cleverness.

ingratitude (in grat´ i tōōd´) *n.* A lack of thankfulness.

insensitive (in sen´ si tiv) *adj.* Not caring; not feeling sympathy.

inspirational (in´ spə rā´ shən əl) *adj.* Causing people to be motivated; providing a good idea.

interpretation (in tûr´ pri tā´ shən) *n.* The playing of a musical piece in a way that shows its meaning.

intoxicated (in tok´ si kā´ tid) *adj.* Highly excited.

intricate (in´ tri kit) *adj.* Made of many parts.

inundation (in´ ən dā´ shən) *n.* A deluge; a flood.

ken (ken) *n.* Knowledge; understanding.

KGB *Komitét gosudárstvennoĭ bezopásnost:* The secret police in the former Soviet Union.

km Kilometer.

knickers (nik´ ərz) *n.* Short, baggy trousers that end at the knees.

kohl (kōl) *n.* A dark powder, used as eyeliner or eyeshadow.

lackey (lak´ ē) *n.* A footman; a manservant.

lapis lazuli (lap´ is laz´ ōō lē) *n.* A deep blue semiprecious gemstone.

lave (lāv) *v.* To wash; to bathe.

lectern (lek´ tərn) *n.* A podium; a tall, narrow piece of furniture with a slanted top, which a speaker stands behind.

logically (loj´ i kə lē) *adv.* In a reasonable way.

lotus (lō´ təs) *n.* A kind of water lily that grows in Egypt and Asia.

lute (lōōt) *n.* An old-time stringed instrument like a guitar.

lyre (līr) *n.* A small harp used in ancient times.

Pronunciation Key: at; lāte; câre;
fäther; set; mē; it; kīte; ox; rōse; ô in
bought; coin; bŏŏk; tōō; form; out; up;
tûrn; ə sound in about, chicken, pencil,
cannon, circus; chair; hw in which;
ring; shop; thin; ŧhere; zh in treasure.

magma (mag´ mə) *n.* The molten material that pours out of a volcano and hardens to become rock.

mandolin (man´ dl in) *n.* A stringed musical instrument.

Marseillaise (mär´ sə lāz´) *n.* The national anthem of France.

mason (mā´ sən) *n.* A builder in stone, bricks, and tile.

melancholy (mel´ ən kol´ ē) *adj.* Sad; moody.

mesa (mā´ sə) *n.* High, flat land like a plateau, but smaller.

mildew (mil´ dōō´) *v.* To grow a coating of fuzzy mold.

minstrel (min´ strəl) *n.* A bard; one who sings or recites poems.

mirage (mi räzh´) *n.* Something that appears but is not really there.

Molotov cocktail (mol´ ə tôf kok´ tāl) *n.* A crude bomb that is thrown by hand.

moonstone (mōōn´ stōn´) *n.* A pearly blue stone.

moonstruck (mōōn´ struk´) *adj.* Crazed as a result of the moon's influence.

motley (mot´ lē) *adj.* Many-colored.

myriad (mir´ ē əd) *n.* An immense number.

myrrh (mûr) *n.* A fragrant, bitter resin used in medicine, perfumes, and incense.

namesake (nām´ sāk´) *n.* One who is named after another.

nanny (nan´ ē) *n.* A woman hired to take care of a child.

nary (nâr´ ē) *adj.* Not any.

nationalist (nash´ ə nl ist´) *adj.* Patriotic; supporting one's country.

noncommittal (non´ kə mit´ l) *adj.* Having no point of view; giving no opinion.

nymph (nimf) *n.* A goddess of the sea, woods, or waters.

obbligato (ob´ li gä´ tō) *n.* The music of a single instrument that is playing to accompany a solo.

obelisk (ob´ ə lisk) *n.* A tall stone monument that is narrower at the top.

oblivion (ə bliv´ ē ən) *n.* The state of being unknown or totally forgotten.

obscurity (əb skyo͝or´ i tē) *n.* The state of being unknown.

observatory (əb zûr´ və tor´ ē) *n.* A place that is designed for astronomers to study the stars.

offhanded (ôf´ han´ did) *adj.* Easygoing; careless; casual.

option (op´ shən) *n.* A choice.

organ (or´ gən) *n.* A newspaper that prints information for a political group.

ornamentation (or´ nə men tā´ shən) *n.* Something used to add beauty.

outing (ou´ ting) *n.* A trip for pleasure.

palanquin (pal´ ən kēn´) *n.* An enclosed structure stretched across four poles in which a person rides while four people carry the poles.

pallor (pal´ ər) *n.* Paleness.

palsy (pôl´ sē) *n.* Paralysis; numbness.

patron (pā´ trən) *n.* One who supports an artist by giving money.

patronage (pā´ trə nij) *n.* The attitude that one is granting a favor.

petition (pə tish´ ən) *n.* A written request to the government.

piñon (pin´ yən) *n.* A kind of pine tree with seeds that can be eaten.

pitiless (pit´ i lis) *adj.* Showing no mercy.

plaintive (plān´ tiv) *adj.* Expressing sadness; mournful.

plaited (plā´ tid) *adj.* Twined; braided.

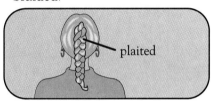

plaited

plateau (pla tō´) *n.* A tract of high, flat land; a tableland.

polecat (pōl´ kat) *n.* A skunk.

porcelain (por´ sə lin) *n.* A ceramic material that can almost be seen through.

pound (pound) *n.* A unit of money in England.

prehistoric (prē´ hi stor´ ik) *adj.* Belonging to a time before history was written down; very early in the history of humans.

première (pri mēr´) *n.* The first public performance of a work.

---

presume (pri zōōm´) *v.* To take for granted; to suppose.

prodigious (prə dij´ əs) *adj.* Enormous; monstrous.

prodigy (prod´ i jē) *n.* A child with extraordinary talent.

profound (prə found´) *adj.* 1. Deep; bottomless. 2. Of deep meaning.

prose (prōz) *n.* Written language that is not verse.

prostrate (pros´ trāt) *adj.* Lying flat.

pueblo (pweb´ lō) *n.* A group of adobe dwellings set into cliffs and reached by ladders.

pumice (pum´ is) *n.* Light, porous lava.

purge (pûrj) *v.* To get rid of undesirable people. —*n.* The removal of some members of a political organization.

putsch (pŏŏch) *n.* A sudden revolt; a political uprising.

quell (kwel) *v.* To overcome by force; to crush.

queue (kyōō) *n.* A line.

rank (rangk) *adj.* Absolute; complete.

ravishing (rav´ i shing) *adj.* Extremely beautiful.

reap (rēp) *v.* To cut grain.

receipts (ri sēts´) *n.* The amount received; income.

reformer (ri for´ mər) *n.* A person who brings about change for the better.

regulate (reg´ yə lāt´) *v.* To adjust something to make it accurate.

relativity (rel´ ə tiv´ i tē) *n.* A theory that says the values of certain things are not absolute, but change according to different points of view. Those things whose values can be changed are time, space, velocity, motion, and mass.

relic (rel´ ik) *n.* A surviving trace of something past or dead.

republic (ri pub´ lik) *n.* A state or body of citizens.

resistance (ri zis´ təns) *n.* Opposition.

restrain (ri strān´) *v.* To hold back; to control.

resurrection (rez´ ə rek´ shən) *n.*
usually capitalized. The act of
Christ rising from the dead.

retaining wall (ri tān´ ing wôl´) *n.*
A wall constructed to keep earth
from pouring over it.

reveille (rev´ ə lē) *n.* A bugle or
drum signal used to call soldiers
together in the morning.

revelation (rev´ ə lā´ shən) *n.*
Something that had not been
known before.

ridicule (rid´ i kyo͞ol´) *v.* To make
fun of; to mock.

rivet (riv´ it) *v.* To have one's
complete attention.

rural (ro͝or´ əl) *adj.* Having to do
with the countryside.

sanctity (sangk´ ti tē) *n.* A sacred
or holy nature.

score (skor) *n.* A musical
composition.

scribe (skrīb) *n.* A clerk with
official status.

seditious (si dish´ əs) *adj.* Disloyal;
unpatriotic.

shirtwaist (shûrt´ wāst´) *n.* A
woman's blouse or dress with a
tailored front like a shirt.

shortwave radio (short´ wāv
rā´ dē ō) *n.* A radio that sends and
receives shortwaves, which are
used for long-distance
transmitting.

sickle (sik´ əl) *n.* A grain-cutting
implement with a large curved
blade.

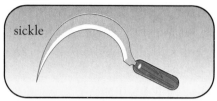

sickle

sinfonia (sin fō nē´ ə) *n.* A
symphony, or instrumental piece,
played as an introduction to an
opera or oratorio.

skein (skān) *n.* Yarn or thread
wound in a coil.

slather (slath´ ər) *v.* To spread.

solace (sol´ is) *n.* Comfort;
consolation.

solar (sō´ lər) *adj.* Concerning the
sun.

solidarity (sol´ i dar´ i tē) *n.* Unity;
a sticking together.

solitary (sol´ i ter´ ē) *adj.* Alone.

soulful (sōl´ fəl) *adj.* Having deep
feeling.

spa (spä) *n.* A health resort that
has a mineral spring.

spawn (spôn) *v.* To give rise to.

spectacle (spek´ tə kəl) *n.* An
impressive public display.

Pronunciation Key: at; lāte; câre; fäther; set; mē; it; kīte; ox; rōse; ô in bought; coin; bŏŏk; tōō; form; out; up; tûrn; ə sound in about, chicken, pencil, cannon, circus; chair; hw in which; ring; shop; thin; there; zh in treasure.

sphere (sfēr) *n.* The area or environment of a person's life.

spiritless (spir´ it lis) *adj.* Without enthusiasm.

splice (splīs) *v.* To join; to connect.

stipend (stī´ pend) *n.* A fixed salary.

stucco (stuk´ ō) *n.* Plaster for covering outer walls.

Styx (stiks) *n.* In Greek mythology, the river that dead souls crossed.

subdivision (sub´ di vizh´ ən) *n.* A piece of land broken into separate lots for houses.

suffragist (suf´ rə jist) *n.* One who believes that women should have the right to vote.

sulphur or **sulfur** (sul´ fər) *n.* A yellow mineral substance with a sharp odor, used in medicine and chemistry.

summit (sum´ it) *n.* The highest point; the top.

sweatlodge (swet´ loj´) *n.* A building in which Native

Americans cleansed themselves both spiritually and physically.

syncopated (sing´ kə pā´ tid) *adj.* Having a shortened, quick-sounding rhythm.

tango (tang´ gō) *n.* The music for a Latin-American ballroom dance.

tenement (ten´ ə mənt) *n.* A run-down and crowded apartment building in a poor section of a city.

theory (thē´ ə rē) *n.* The principles, or rules, and the methods, or techniques, of a science or an art.

timidity (ti mid´ i tē) *n.* Shyness; fright.

tome (tōm) *n.* A large book; a scholarly book.

totalitarian (tō tal´ i târ´ ē ən) *adj.* Authoritarian; controlling.

transform (trans form´) *v.* To change completely.

treat (trēt) *v.* To negotiate; to try to reach a settlement.

trill (tril) *n.* A musical sound that goes quickly back and forth between two notes.

tripe (trīp) *n. slang.* Something that is worthless.

trowel (trou´ əl) *n.* A short-handled tool for spreading mortar or digging up plants.

turquoise (tûr´ koiz) *n.* A semiprecious stone of bluish-green color.

unabashed (un´ ə basht´) *adj.* Bold; not embarrassed or ashamed.

uncommitted (un´ kə mit´ id) *adj.* Not promised or bound to support a specific cause.

unguent (ung´ gwənt) *n.* An ointment or a salve, as a lotion.

unique (yo͞o nēk´) *adj.* Having no equal; one of a kind.

universal (yo͞o´ nə vûr´ səl) *adj.* Known everywhere; belonging to everyone.

unlikeliest (un līk´ lē əst) *adj.* The least likely.

unprecedented (un pres´ i den´ tid) *adj.* Having never happened before.

upright (up´ rīt´) *n.* A type of piano.

urn (ûrn) *n.* A large vase.

vainglorious (vān glor´ ē əs) *adj.* Boastful; having too much pride.

vale (vāl) *n.* A valley.

venerate (ven´ ə rāt´) *v.* To respect or treat with reverence.

waif (wāf) *n.* A homeless child.

wash (wosh) *n.* An area of dry land that has been shaped partly by the action of water moving over it.

wayfaring (wā´ fâr´ ing) *adj.* Traveling.

windfall (wind´ fôl´) *n.* An unexpected gain.

X-ray (eks´ rā´) *n.* A ray, or beam, that goes through solid substances and allows photographs to be taken of broken bones or other unseen objects.

yon (yon) *adj. archaic.* Yonder; over there.

yucca (yuk´ ə) *n.* A plant with white flowers and large leaves shaped like swords in a cluster.

yucca

zealot (zel´ ət) *n.* A person who shows too much enthusiasm for a cause.

continued from page 5